Choosing Autism Interventi

© Research Autism and Autism

Research Autism and Autism V
rights in accordance with the (
(1988) to be identified as the

ir
Act

Published by:
Pavilion Publishing and Media Ltd
Rayford House, School Road, Hove, BN3 5HX
Tel: 01273 434 943
Fax: 01273 227 308
Email: info@pavpub.com

Published April 2015. Reprinted October 2015.
Review date April 2020.

A catalogue record for this book is available from the British
Library.

ISBN: 978-1-910366-76-9

Authors: Bernard Fleming (Research Autism), Elisabeth Hurley
(Autism West Midlands) and the Goth (James Mason)

Editor: Catherine Ansell-Jones, Pavilion Publishing and Media Ltd

Cover design: Emma Dawe, Pavilion Publishing and Media Ltd

Images: Photographs reproduced with permission from the
National Autistic Society

Layout design: Emma Dawe, Pavilion Publishing and Media Ltd

Printing: Short Run Press Limited

What people say about this book

'As someone diagnosed with autism who also has children with autism, I found this book very informative, easy to read, honest, well written and unbiased. It is a great resource for newly diagnosed people, parents, adults, professionals and anyone with an interest in the facts about autism. It invites the reader to learn all they can about making decisions regarding autism and autism interventions. It is empowering and powerful in many ways.'

Shell Spectrum, a parent on the autism spectrum

'This book is necessary and long overdue for parents. It is well structured with clear and easy to follow text, full of relevant and unambiguous information. There is a good balance of the pros and cons of an intervention supported by current research with good explanations of medical and technical terminology.'

Gen Hartup, mother of two children on the autism spectrum

'I think this is a very useful book for people with autism and their families trying to navigate the avalanche of information available. Honest and unbiased, it is a great starting point to understanding the complexities of the different therapies and the reality of the research behind them.'

Karen Wilmshurst, Advocacy Services Manager, Autism Wessex

Contents

Foreword

In the UK it can be hard enough – still – to access a diagnosis of autism, and even harder to access the correct educational and social support that is the statutory right of every person with a disability. Over the 30-odd years I've been involved with autism I have had countless people tell me that they just didn't know which way to turn to get the most effective support for themselves or their child, and it's easy to understand why so many look to unconventional theories, alternative therapies and unresearched interventions. As a doctor's daughter, naturally I fear for those who make such uninformed choices and only wish that everyone had access to someone with genuine understanding and knowledge of this condition and its possible interventions. It's vital that a fully informed choice is made and it isn't simple: every person with autism will show the effects of their condition differently and there will never be one solution that will work for all.

There are many unsubstantiated 'treatments' – even 'cures' – that are suggested for autism (as, indeed, they are for so many other conditions), from manipulation of various parts of the body to the channelling of 'energy fields'; from the removal of mercury from the body to changes in diet. Few of these therapies are supported by any clinical research, but you can easily see how a desperate parent might leap at the idea of some 'miracle cure' highlighted in one of the tabloids – something that sadly happens only too often. Some of these interventions are positively harmful, others are at best ineffective and many are extremely expensive.

That's where this excellent book comes in. Research Autism, the charity behind it, was set up to try to redress the balance and to investigate and provide funds for research into the interventions suggested for autism. I have been involved since its launch in 2003 and have seen the wonderful work it does in negotiating the minefield of claims surrounding the complexities of autism. I'm delighted that they have now published some of the information that has been amassed over the years in this clear and useful guide, which I am sure will be of immense help, not only to families and friends, but also to many people on the spectrum themselves.

In a user-friendly and accessible way it provides easy to understand descriptions of some of the most commonly used autism treatments and therapies together with objective and unbiased evaluations based on proper scientific research, making it easy to understand and very helpful in trying to make decisions on just which intervention might be useful. It also summarises best practice guidance from the National Institute for Health and Care Excellence (NICE).

This is currently the only book on autism treatments and therapies that meets the requirements of the NHS Information Standard, which means that the information is clear, accurate, balanced, evidence based and up to date. It won't, of course, tell you everything you need to know about autism treatments and therapies – no single book could ever hope to do that. But it's a really good place to start and I know that anyone with an interest in this complex condition will find it as informative as I did.

The fight continues to ensure that everyone on the autistic spectrum is able to lead a life of dignity and fulfilment. I believe that this book will play an important part in that fight.

Jane Asher

Patron, Research Autism

Preface

Although autism resides in an individual, it touches the lives of everyone around them – families, friends, service providers and wider society. As knowledge and awareness of autism grows, so does the need for access to the best available evidence-based information about how people with autism and their families can be supported in the most appropriate way.

We therefore warmly welcome the publication of this new book on choosing the right autism interventions, which aims to cut through the voluminous and sometimes baffling array of information that exists 'out there' about autism treatments, therapies and approaches.

Since they were founded, both Research Autism and Autism West Midlands have made a significant impact on the autism landscape. Research Autism's research and information programmes, driven directly by the needs of the autism community, have set the agenda in terms of securing better outcomes for people with autism and their families, while Autism West Midlands' specialist services, increasing range of publications and pioneering employment support are contributing to good practice nationwide.

Both of our organisations share a vision to improve the inclusion, quality of life and outlook of people with autism. This book gives practical meaning to that vision by providing guidance to enable those living with the condition to make informed choices about interventions.

It is our firm belief that good services, high quality research, and impartial information have the power to change lives for the better. We believe that this book makes a positive contribution to achieving this outcome for autistic people and their families.

Deepa Korea, Chief Executive Research Autism and **Jonathan Shephard**, Chief Executive, Autism West Midlands

Introduction

Background

In recent years the number of people diagnosed with autism has risen significantly, although no one knows if this is due to a real rise in the number of people on the autism spectrum, greater awareness of autism by healthcare professionals, or a change in the measures used to diagnose autism (1).

The rise in diagnosis has been matched by a bewildering increase in the number and types of treatments and therapies. For example, the Research Autism website lists more than 1,000 different interventions, including applied behaviour analysis (ABA), chelation, dramatherapy, the gluten-free diet, Lego therapy, sensory integration training, swimming with dolphins, and vitamin supplements (2).

Unfortunately, some treatments and therapies are expensive, time consuming and potentially hazardous. Furthermore, currently very little scientific research supports the use of many interventions, despite extravagant and misleading claims about some of them.

> 'There is a desperate need for parents to know where to turn for impartial advice on the various therapies. After our son was diagnosed we would literally try everything we could lay our hands on that promised to help. We followed up leads from the internet and popular press and it seemed that many of the professionals were as much in the dark as we were. We now know that many of the things on offer were a waste of time; some little more than snake oil treatments.' Alex, parent of six-year-old Shaun (3).

Purpose of this book

We try to provide an unbiased source of information that is so desperately needed by parents like Alex.

Choosing Autism Interventions: A Research-Based Guide © Research Autism and Autism West Midlands

This is what we're trying to do:

- describe some of the interventions commonly used in the UK
- evaluate those treatments and therapies based on the published scientific research
- summarise guidance from the National Institute for Health and Care Excellence
- suggest some key questions you may like to ask about any intervention or research study
- list some useful resources including websites and publications.

We are not trying to:

- provide a comprehensive list of every treatment
- promote or criticise a particular type or group of therapies
- tell you which treatment or therapy you should or should not use
- tell you how to implement a specific treatment or therapy.

Quality

This book carries the NHS Information Standard quality mark. The quality mark is a quick and easy way for you to identify reliable and trustworthy sources of information. It means you can trust what we say because we are not trying to sell you anything or tell you what you should or should not do. It also means that we have tried to provide the information in a clear and user-friendly manner (4).

Limitations

So much information on interventions is available that it would be impractical to try and put it all in one book. So we have tried to only include information about the most commonly used interventions, the major sources of research evidence, the most robust clinical guidance, and so on. We also know that, as soon as this book is published, new research may come out which appears to contradict or modify findings from the existing research. We would urge you to keep an eye on the Autism West Midlands website, the Research Autism website, and the other resources listed in Appendix 6 of this book if you wish to be kept up to date on the best evidence.

Disclaimer

The information we present in this book is designed to support, not replace, the relationship that exists between you and your healthcare or service provider. The information has been written by non-medically qualified individuals, unless we specifically state otherwise. Any such information should therefore be treated with care.

The information in this book is not intended to act as a recommendation on whether a specific individual on the autism spectrum should or should not use an intervention. The outcome of any intervention will depend on a range of factors, including the individual's needs and abilities, and on the way in which the intervention is implemented.

The information in this book was correct at the time of publication in April 2015. To see if there is a later version of this book please see www.researchautism.net/our-publications

References

1. Anderson C (2014) *Careful Counting: How many people have an ASD?* Baltimore, MD: IAN Network.

2. Research Autism (2014a) Alphabetic list of interventions, treatments and therapies [online]. Available at: www.researchautism.net/alphabetic-list-interventions (accessed January 13, 2015).

3. Research Autism (2014b) *Research Autism* [online]. London, UK: Research Autism.

4. The Information Standard (2014) *About the Information Standard.* London, UK: The Information Standard.

How to use this book

This section will help you get the best out of this book.

Content

Four main sections make up this book:

1. **Key information:** Chapters 1–4 provide information on: autism, the issues faced by people on the autism spectrum, interventions designed to help people on the autism spectrum, how scientists evaluate those interventions.

2. **Interventions:** Chapters 5–26 provide details about the different types of intervention, along with an evaluation of the evidence base behind each type of intervention. Each of these chapters also provides information about the likely costs and time required to undertake this type of intervention; the supply and regulation (quality control) of this type of intervention; the risks of this type of intervention. Chapter 27 concludes this section.

3. **Making the decision:** This section provides you with some tools that may help you when you are deciding which interventions, if any, to use. The tools include: further details on the key principles that we believe any intervention should follow; key questions that you may like to ask about any intervention; red flags (signs that an intervention is not what it seems); key questions you may like to ask about research papers; a summary of the most recent guidance from the National Institute for Health and Care Excellence.

4. **Appendices:** The appendices provide a range of other information that we hope you will find useful. They include personal perspectives of living with autism, as well as lists of useful organisations, websites and publications.

Design

We have tried to design this book so that it is easy to read, it is easy to find what you are looking for, and you don't have to read the whole thing if you don't want to. So:

- we have included a main index (Appendix 7), a separate index of interventions (Appendix 8) and a glossary (Appendix 4)
- we have summarised some of the key information in boxes so that you don't have to read the whole chapter
- we have used colour to differentiate between the sections
- we have repeated some of the key messages throughout the book
- we have not tried to tell you everything you could possibly want to know about each intervention (there just isn't room in a publication like this)
- we have provided information about additional resources including other publications, websites and organisations.

Terminology

Our preferred term for the people we refer to most in this book is 'people on the autism spectrum'. We use this term because we think that it is the most helpful, as it tells you that each person on the autism spectrum is a unique individual. We know that some people prefer other terms such as 'autistic people' or 'people with autism', and this is fine.

Our preferred term for the treatments, therapies and services people on the autism spectrum may receive is 'interventions'. We use this term because it covers a wide range of approaches. It is also the term used by most professionals.

What works and doesn't work?

As you read this book, you will see very quickly that many interventions have little or no research evidence to show that they are effective. This doesn't mean that they do not work; it may simply mean that more research is required to find out if they do.

Choosing Autism Interventions: A Research-Based Guide © Research Autism and Autism West Midlands

Where an intervention works for some people, this does not mean that it will work for everyone on the autism spectrum, because each person on the spectrum is unique. Also, the fact that an intervention works in a research setting does not mean that it will work in the real world.

Evidence

Our evaluation of the evidence for the interventions described in this book is based on our own systematic literature reviews of research studies published in English-language, peer-reviewed journals. Our searches covered a range of databases including the Cochrane Collaboration, ERIC, Psychinfo, PubMed, and the Research Autism publications database.

We also looked at clinical guidance from appropriate agencies such as NICE and best practice statements from other agencies where we thought this was appropriate.

Please see Appendix 3 for more information on what our levels of evidence mean.

Limitations

This book, like every book on autism or on interventions, has some limitations.

Coverage: we have not tried to describe every single intervention currently being used to help people on the autism spectrum. Nor have we described any intervention in great detail, or told you how to implement it, or told you whether it is appropriate for different people on the spectrum.

Up-to-dateness: the information in this book, including our evaluations of different interventions, was correct at the time of publication in April 2015. However research on autism is being published all the time. For details of the latest research on autism please see www.researchautism.net/latest-publications.

Key principles for autism interventions

There are hundreds of interventions designed to help people on the autism spectrum. There are thousands of research studies looking at those interventions, with more studies coming out every day.

A book of this size can only look at some of those interventions and some of that research. It can't, of course, look at research that was published after this book was published.

So, we have written down some key principles that we hope may help you decide which interventions, if any, you wish to use.

We believe that any intervention designed to help people on the autism spectrum should follow most, if not all, of these principles.

1. The intervention is based on a good understanding of autism.

2. The people who deliver the intervention know the person well and respect their feelings and views.

3. The person's capacity for consent is taken into account.

4. The intervention is adapted to the needs of the person receiving it.

5. The intervention is based on a theory that is logical and scientifically feasible.

6. Research evidence shows the intervention can work for people on the autism spectrum.

7. The intervention works in the real world, not just in a research laboratory.

8. The intervention is delivered by, or supported by, appropriately qualified and experienced professionals.

9. The people delivering the intervention follow established guidance.

10. The intervention is carefully monitored and reviewed on a regular basis.

11. The intervention provides significant benefits.

12. The intervention does not cause significant physical or emotional harm.

13. The benefits outweigh any costs (including risks).

14. The intervention is good value for the money and time invested.

Further information

In this book: Please see a detailed explanation of these principles and why we think they are important on page 287.

Key information

Introduction

This section provides information on autism, the issues faced by people on the autism spectrum, interventions designed to help people on the autism spectrum and how scientists evaluate interventions.

Chapter 1:
What is autism?

Introduction

You may already know something about autism, but in case you don't, and so that you have as much of the information you need in one book, we look at the core features of autism and how individuals on the spectrum vary one from another. We look at the number of people on the autism spectrum, the causes of autism, and when autism begins. We also consider the different types of autism and how they are categorised and diagnosed. We end with a discussion of what happens to people on the autism spectrum as they get older and whether autism is a disability or a difference.

Core features

Scientists classify autism as a neurodevelopmental disorder, that is, a condition which affects the development of the brain (1). Individuals on the autism spectrum vary enormously from each other but they all share the two 'core' features of autism (2):

- Persistent difficulties with social communication and social interaction. For example, they may find it hard to begin or carry on a conversation, they may not understand social rules such as how far to stand from somebody else, or they may find it difficult to make friends.
- Restricted, repetitive patterns of behaviour, interests, or activities. For example, they may develop an overwhelming interest in something, they may follow inflexible routines or rituals, they may make repetitive body movements, or they may be hypersensitive to certain sounds.

Individuals on the autism spectrum also face many other issues, problems and challenges on a day-to-day basis which are covered in more detail in Chapter 2 (see page 27).

Autism is a spectrum

People on the autism spectrum can be very different from each other, even though they share the core features of autism. For example, some people may have little or no speech, whereas others may be highly articulate, although their speech may be stilted, and they may not have mastered the art of conversation (taking turns during conversations and recognising the conventions of a conversation) (3).

Some people with autism may take language very literally – for example misunderstanding 'It's raining cats and dogs' – while others may understand that this is a metaphor, but still think in very literal terms, for example by assuming that a person will do precisely what they say they will do.

Some people may expect a person to arrive at the exact time they said they would arrive, and become anxious if they don't. Other people may be more flexible.

Some people with autism have an uneven profile of abilities (see Figure 1.1). This means that they may be very good at certain things (for example, social interaction), but may not be very good at other things (for example, thinking flexibly).

The important thing to remember is that every person with autism is different. This has an impact on the interventions that are used for these people, and whether they will work. We discuss this in Chapter 3 (see page 38).

Numbers and statistics

There are approximately 700,000 people in the UK on the autism spectrum – over one per cent of the population. However, some people believe the numbers may be higher than this (4–6).

The number of people on the autism spectrum appears to have risen dramatically over the past two decades, although the reasons for this are unclear. Most of the increase may be explained by increased awareness of autism, changing diagnostic criteria, better diagnosis, and a phenomenon known as 'diagnostic substitution' (where the prevalence of one condition increases while another decreases because it is discovered that people were misdiagnosed, so their diagnosis is changed) (7). There may also be a small increase in the actual number of people on the autism spectrum.

Figure 1.1: Profile of abilities

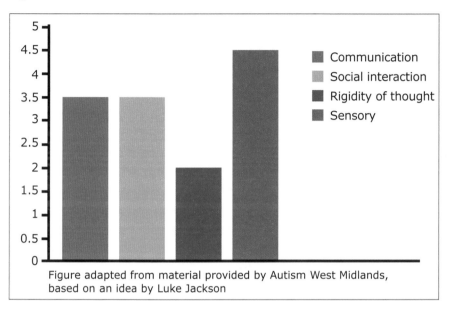

Figure adapted from material provided by Autism West Midlands, based on an idea by Luke Jackson

Autism is believed to affect on average four times as many men as women (8). However, this depends on the level of ability, with only twice as many men affected as women if they have severe learning disabilities and around 10 times as many men affected as women in Asperger syndrome (9). This may partly be due to men being more prone to autism, as seen in some genetic studies (10). But it is also partly due to a current lack of knowledge of how autism shows itself in women (11). Women with autism are often more easily able to hide their difficulties and blend in. However, the efforts they make to do this can be exhausting and can result in mental health problems. Furthermore, much of our knowledge of autism is based on observation and study of boys – diagnostic criteria and assessment tools are all designed based on a male picture of autism, making it all too easy to miss women and girls at diagnosis.

Little is known about the prevalence of autism in older age groups. Studies suggest that the prevalence of autism is similar across age groups which implies that over one per cent of the older population may also have autism (12). However, this group has not received much attention. It is only recently, as the original cases of autism diagnosed in the 1940s, 1950s and 1960s reach old age, that the needs of the ageing autism population are being considered. Much more needs to be done, as many older people are currently undiagnosed and there is very little specific guidance on supporting older people with autism (13).

Causes

Autism has no single cause. Most researchers believe that autism has a variety of causes, which are likely to be a complex mix of genetic and environmental factors which may affect a variety of parts of the brain. The Medical Research Council reported:

'Research over the last half century has established autism as a neurodevelopmental disorder. Early suggestions that ASDs [autism spectrum disorders] might result from abnormal parenting have been abandoned in the face of overwhelming evidence for a biological basis and a strong genetic component. Most researchers believe that ASDs have a variety of causes, perhaps all affecting the same brain systems, or impeding development through disruption of different abilities necessary for social and communicative development. Whether environmental factors interact with genetic susceptibility is as yet unclear.' (14)

Onset and regression

According to the National Institute for Health and Care Excellence (NICE) autism is present from early childhood, although features may not always be visible until social demands exceed a child's capabilities. For example, features may become apparent when starting at nursery or school or moving to secondary school. Some parents may notice that their child is different from birth while others may not notice until they are older (15).

Some children (between one fifth and one third of children) appear to develop normally and then regress, losing skills they previously had. According to NICE, this usually occurs in the second year of life for unknown reasons (15). Regression which occurs after the age of three years is very rare and is termed 'childhood disintegrative disorder'.

Diagnosis

Getting a diagnosis of autism can be a positive thing as it can provide an explanation for some of the difficulties a person may be experiencing, as well as allowing access to services and support. The process of getting a diagnosis varies from country to country and sometimes even within the same country.

In the UK, the first step of the process is to contact a GP, health visitor or special educational needs co-ordinator (SENCO) who will then refer you to specialist diagnostic services. However this is not always a straightforward process as some professionals may be reluctant to start the process, and there may be a lack of specialist diagnostic services in some areas, especially for adults (16).

Diagnostic tools

The diagnostic assessment can take some time. It is based on developmental history and the use of various tools to assess areas of difficulty. A number of 'gold standard' tools such as the Autism Diagnostic Observation Schedule (ADOS) and the Autism Diagnostic Interview-Revised (ADI-R) are used, but no tool will be used by everyone, so your diagnosis session may be different.

In adults, diagnosis can be more challenging as there are fewer diagnostic tools that are appropriate for adults. Furthermore, it can be harder to obtain a developmental history because the person with autism may not have anyone who can give details of their early childhood (16).

Diagnostic manuals

Two major diagnostic manuals are used to diagnose autism, and both are reviewed and updated on a regular basis:

- The Diagnostic and Statistical Manual of Mental Disorders (DSM) is mainly used in the USA and the latest version, DSM-5, was updated in May 2013.
- The International Classification of Diseases (ICD) is mainly used in Europe and the latest version, ICD-10, is due to be updated in 2017 (17).

The recent update of the DSM means that the diagnostic criteria for autism in the two manuals are currently different. The ICD-10 uses three areas of difficulty to define autism (the triad of impairments): difficulties in social interaction, difficulties in social communication and repetitive and restrictive behaviours (18). The DSM-5, on the other hand, uses two broad categories – difficulties in social communication and social interaction, and repetitive and restrictive behaviours and sensory issues (2).

We use the DSM-5 criteria in this book since we believe that when the ICD is revised it will probably also switch to two, rather than three, core features of autism.

Specific diagnoses

The current version of the Diagnostic and Statistical Manual of Mental Disorders, DSM-5, uses the 'umbrella term' of 'autism spectrum disorder' (ASD) to describe any form of autism. The previous version, DSM-IV, broke down autism into various sub-groups including autistic disorder, Asperger syndrome, and pervasive developmental disorders not otherwise specified (19). This is also still the case in the ICD-10.

- Autistic disorder (also known as autism, classic autism or Kanner's autism) – describes individuals who have the core features of autism including a clinically significant delay in language.
- Asperger syndrome (also known as Asperger's disorder) – describes individuals with no clinically significant delay in language but who still have the core features of autism. People with Asperger syndrome are often highly intelligent.

- Pervasive developmental disorders not otherwise specified (also known as PDD-NOS) – describes individuals who do not fit into the diagnosis of either autistic disorder or Asperger syndrome but who do have clear features of autism which warrant a diagnosis (18).

The recent change to the Diagnostic and Statistical Manual of Mental Disorders has caused some controversy and some people are worried that the new diagnostic criteria will mean that some individuals with Asperger syndrome or PDD-NOS will no longer qualify for a diagnosis of autism and therefore not receive the services to which they are entitled (20).

Please note: we use the term 'people on the autism spectrum' to refer to anyone with a diagnosis or suspected diagnosis of any kind of autism.

Levels of ability

Some people describe individuals on the autism spectrum as either 'high-functioning' or 'low-functioning' (sometimes known as 'severe' autism).

People with high-functioning autism have a non-verbal IQ of 70 or more, while people with low-functioning autism have a non-verbal IQ lower than 70 (and may also be non-verbal or have very limited speech).

High-functioning autism and Asperger syndrome may be the same thing (this is still being debated). Most research has not shown enough difference to justify it being a separate diagnosis. However, some researchers do believe high-functioning autism and Asperger syndrome are different and need to be separated at diagnosis.

The terms 'high-functioning' and 'low-functioning' autism are also debated. Some people say they are not useful or they are insulting. For example, some individuals classified as having 'severe' autism may be highly intelligent and can function very well with the right kind of support. Some 'high-functioning' individuals on the autism spectrum, on the other hand, may face considerable difficulties which are overlooked because they appear to be coping (21, 22).

Outcomes

When describing autism, the focus tends to be on a person's difficulties. However, people with autism often have significant strengths such as a good eye for detail, an excellent memory for facts and figures and a high level of accuracy and reliability. Some also have considerable creative talent.

People with autism often have significant problems and other conditions such as mental health problems, epilepsy, sensory issues and gastrointestinal problems. These can lead to difficulties at school, in the workplace or making friends. However, with the right support tailored to individual needs, some people with autism can lead relatively independent lives. Others will continue to need support and understanding throughout their lives (15, 23).

Neurodiversity

Some people on the autism spectrum claim that autism is not a disorder but simply an expression of neurodiversity. In other words, autism is a difference, not a disorder (24).

'People need to get over the idea that the neuro-typical way is 'right' and any other way is 'wrong'. The AS way is just as valid – in fact better in some respects. We should be accepted in our own right and the emphasis should be on educating NTs [neurotypicals] not to be so discriminatory and to get over the absurd and offensive idea that they are better than anyone else. People with AS don't need to be 'cured' or trained as to how to 'pretend' to be normal – it is the 'normal' people who need to learn that, contrary to what they think, they are not the pinnacle of God's creation and that there is in fact a lot they could learn from Aspies. They need to be taught not to be prejudiced and discriminatory and to accept and accommodate us for who we are.' (25)

References

1. Lai M-C, Lombardo M V & Baron-Cohen S (2014) Autism. *Lancet* **383** 896–910.

2. American Psychiatric Association (2013) *Diagnostic and Statistical Manual of Mental Disorders – DSM-5*. Washington DC: American Psychiatric Association.

3. Attwood T (2007) Language. In T Attwood *The Complete Guide to Asperger's Syndrome* (pp 202–227). London:Jessica Kingsley Publishers.

4. Brugha TS, Cooper SA, McManus S, Purdon S, Smith J, Scott FJ, Spiers N & Tyrer F (2012) *Estimating the Prevalence of Autism Spectrum Conditions in Adults: Extending the 2007 Adult Psychiatric Morbidity Survey*. London: The NHS Information Centre.

5. Developmental Disabilities Monitoring Network Surveillance Year 2010 Principle Investigators, CDC (2014) Prevalence of autism spectrum disorder among children aged 8 years-autism and developmental disabilities monitoring network, 11 sites, United States, 2010. *Morbidity and Mortality Weekly Report Surveillance Summary* **63** 1–21.

6. Kim Y, Leventhal BL, Koh YJ, Fombonne E, Laska E, Lim EC, Cheon KA, Kim SJ, Kim YK, Lee H, Song DH & Grinker RR (2011) Prevalence of autism spectrum disorders in a total population sample. *American Journal of Psychiatry* **168** 904–912.

7. Bishop DVM, Whitehouse AJO, Watt HJ & Line EA (2008) Autism and diagnostic substitution: evidence from a study of adults with a history of developmental language disorder. *Developmental Medicine and Child Neurology* **50** 341–345.

8. Fombonne E (2005) The changing epidemiology of autism. *Journal of Applied Research in Intellectual Disabilities* **18** 281–294.

9. Fombonne E (2003) Epidemiological surveys of autism and other pervasive developmental disorders: an update. *Journal of Autism and Developmental Disorders* **33** 365–382.

10. Jacquemont S, Coe B, Hersch M, Duyzend MH, Niklas Krumm N, Bergmann S, Beckmann JS, Rosenfeld JA & Eichler EE (2014) A higher mutational burden in females supports a 'female protective model' in neurodevelopmental disorders. *The American Journal of Human Genetics* **94** 415–425.

11. Gould J & Ashton-Smith J (2011) Missed diagnosis or misdiagnosis? Girls and women on the autism spectrum. *Good Autism Practice* **12** 34–41.

12. Brugha TS, McManus S, Bankart J, Scott F, Purdon S, Smith J, Bebbington P, Jenkins R & Meltzer H (2011) Epidemiology of autism spectrum disorders in adults in the community in England. *Archives of General Psychiatry* **68** 459–466.

13. Autism Europe (2013) *Towards a Better Quality of Life: The rights of ageing people with autism*. Brussels, Belgium: Autism Europe.

14. Medical Research Council (2001) *MRC Review of Autism Research: Epidemiology and causes*. London, UK: Medical Research Council.

15. National Institute for Health and Care Excellence (2013) *The Management and Support of Children and Young People on the Autism Spectrum*. London: National Institute for Health and Care Excellence.

16. National Institute for Health and Clinical Excellence (2011) A*utism Diagnosis in Children and Young People: Recognition, referral and diagnosis of children and young people on the autism spectrum*. London: National Institute for Health and Clinical Excellence.

17. World Health Organization (2014) *The International Classification of Diseases, 11th edition.* Revision is due by 2017. Available at: www.who.int/classifications/icd/revision/en/ (accessed January 13, 2015).

18. World Health Organization (1992) *International Classification of Diseases - ICD-10*. Geneva: WHO.

19. American Psychiatric Association (1994) *Diagnostic and Statistical Manual of Mental Disorders - DSM-IV*. Washington DC: American Psychological Association.

20. Volkmar FR & Reichow B (2013) Autism in DSM-5: progress and challenges. *Molecular Autism* **4** 13.

21. Witwer AN & Lecavalier L (2008) Examining the validity of autism spectrum disorder subtypes. *Journal of Autism and Developmental Disorders* **38** 1611–1624.

22. Research Autism (2014) Intellectual ability and autism [online]. Available at: www.researchautism.net/intellectual-ability (accessed January 13, 2015).

23. Levy A & Perry A (2011) Outcomes in adolescents and adults with autism: a review of the literature. *Research in Autism Spectrum Disorders* **5** (4) 1271--1282

24. Kapp SK, Gillespie-Lynch K, Sherman LE & Hutman T (2013) Deficit, difference, or both? Autism and neurodiversity. *Developmental Psychology* **49** 59–71.

25. Beardon L & Edmonds G (2007) *ASPECT Consultancy Report. A national report on the needs of adults with Asperger syndrome*. Sheffield: Sheffield Hallam University.

Chapter 2:
Issues facing people on the autism spectrum

People on the autism spectrum face many issues, challenges and problems. In this chapter, we look at the most common issues, such as cognition, IQ and intelligence. We look at motor skills, sensory sensitivity and everyday skills. We look at co-occurring genetic conditions and medical complaints, developmental disorders and mental health problems. Finally, we look at challenging behaviour, inclusion and exclusion, and the impact that autism has on the rest of the family.

Introduction

People on the autism spectrum (and their relatives and carers) face issues, challenges and problems every day. In some cases, one problem or challenge can make another problem or challenge worse. For example, a number of things can make some people on the autism spectrum very anxious (such as an unexpected change in routine) and anxiety can lead to additional problems (such as challenging behaviour) (1). In other cases, the exact relationship between different issues is unclear. For example, there may be an association between gastrointestinal problems, sensory over-sensitivity and anxiety in some people on the autism spectrum. However, it is not clear which of these problems causes the others or if there is a common underlying cause (2).

It is important to remember that each person on the autism spectrum is a unique individual, with unique needs and abilities. Because of this, they will experience their issues in a unique way or may not experience them at all. Remember that some individuals on the autism spectrum don't think of autism as a problem at all, it's just the way they are.

Cognition

Cognition is sometimes defined as the mental process of knowing, including aspects such as awareness, perception, reasoning, judgment and memory (3).

Many people on the autism spectrum appear to have difficulties with some of these mental processes (4). For example, some autistic individuals appear to have difficulties with connecting past experience with present action, a problem called executive function (5). Executive function includes activities such as planning, working memory, and monitoring actions. Other autistic individuals seem to have difficulties with the ability to understand how other people think and feel, called theory of mind (6).

Many people on the autism spectrum also have extremely strong cognitive skills in one area (such as reasoning) but very poor cognitive skills in another area (such as memory), which is called an uneven cognitive profile (7). Or, even more confusingly, they may have different strengths in the same area (such as good long-term memory but poor short-term memory) (8). This can make it very difficult to judge someone's real level of ability. For example, you might overestimate someone's ability to function in the real world because they have strong cognitive skills in one area but not in another.

IQ and intelligence

Some people on the autism spectrum are described as 'high-functioning', meaning they have an IQ of 70 or more. Some may be highly intelligent, perhaps able to read and write academic research papers or undertake complex programming tasks. However, because they are on the autism spectrum they may struggle to understand social conventions or struggle with tasks that seem relatively simple to other people, such as making a cup of tea or crossing the road by themselves.

Some people on the autism spectrum are described as 'low-functioning', meaning they have an IQ of less than 70. This (less than 70) is one definition of a learning disability. Approximately

50% of young people on the autism spectrum have a learning disability. Many also have one or more specific learning difficulties, that is, difficulties with literacy, numeracy and other academic skills (9).

Motor skills

Motor skills can be defined as the ability to perform complex muscle actions that produce movement. Fine motor skills are small movements like writing and tying shoe laces, gross motor skills are large movements like walking and kicking (10).

Many individuals on the autism spectrum have difficulties with motor skills. For example, some people have a clumsy walk, poor muscle tone, difficulty balancing, poor dexterity or difficulties with planning movements (11).

Some of these difficulties with motor skills may be due to problems with the vestibular sense (the sense of balance in your inner ear) and the proprioception sense (close your eyes and wiggle your fingers: you can feel them moving, and that's proprioception) (11).

Sensory processing

Sensory processing is the ability to take in, integrate and make use of sensory information.

- Hypersensitivity is being over-responsive to sensory stimulation. Some people with autism and hypersensitivity may find certain sounds physically painful or they may not be able to wear certain clothing because they are sensitive to the texture.

- Hyposensitivity is being under-responsive to sensory stimulation. Some people with autism and hyposensitivity may seek out strong flavours, as they find ordinary flavours bland, or they may rock to and fro so that they get a stronger feeling of how they are positioned (12).

People on the autism spectrum can be hypo-sensitive or hyper-sensitive to any of the senses (for example, sight, sound, touch, vision, taste, vestibular or proprioception). People with autism can have any type of sensory issue and any combination of sensory issues (13, 14).

Functional skills

Functional skills are a wide range of skills we all need to survive and thrive. These include everyday skills such as washing, dressing and undressing, preparing and eating food, using the toilet, falling asleep and staying asleep (15).

Many individuals on the autism spectrum struggle with one or more functional skills. For example, an estimated 50–80% of people with autism have sleep problems, significantly more than most other people (9–50%) (16–19). The likelihood of developing sleep problems in autism is not associated with the level of ability, but may be associated with difficulty planning the day, letting go of the memories from their day, anxiety and other symptoms of autism. The underlying reasons for sleep problems will vary from one person to the next but could be due to problems with the way the body clock (the circadian system) works, behavioural problems, co-existing conditions such as anxiety, depression, ADHD and epilepsy, and medication. Sleep problems can lead to changes in daytime behaviour, problems with memory and learning, and stress and tiredness for caretakers (16–19).

Genetic conditions

Genetic conditions occur alongside autism and have a well-established genetic cause. These include fragile-X syndrome and tuberous sclerosis, each of which brings its own challenges.

Fragile-X syndrome is a rare condition that affects two to six per cent of people on the autism spectrum. Fragile-X syndrome is a condition in which the X chromosome has been damaged. It is the most common known cause of inherited learning disabilities. It can cause a wide range of difficulties with learning, as well as social, language, attentional, emotional, and behavioural problems (20).

Tuberous sclerosis is a rare condition that affects between 0.4% and 2.8% of people on the autism spectrum. Tuberous sclerosis causes mainly benign (non-cancerous) tumours to develop all over the body. Tumours can develop on the skin and other parts of the body including the brain, heart, eyes, kidneys and lungs. The benign tumours that develop from tuberous sclerosis can cause a range of other associated health conditions and complications, such as heart and lung problems (21).

Medical conditions

A number of medical conditions commonly occur alongside autism such as epilepsy and gastrointestinal problems.

Between five per cent and 38% of people on the autism spectrum suffer from epilepsy. Individuals who also have a learning disability are even more likely to have epilepsy. Seizures seem to occur most often between the ages of five and 10. Epilepsy is associated with regression, challenging behaviour and sleep problems (22).

Some people with autism also suffer from gastrointestinal problems, which can range from constipation to inflammatory bowel disease and coeliac disease. There is no consensus on the number of people with autism who also have an accompanying gastrointestinal problem but estimates range from 9–70%. What is clear is that any gastrointestinal problem can be experienced in people with autism – no special 'autism' problems exist. Furthermore, some people with autism may not be able to communicate pain or discomfort in the expected way, which could delay the diagnosis of a gastrointestinal problem (23).

Developmental disabilities

Disabilities that begin during the developmental period from pre-birth to early childhood are called developmental disabilities, although they usually last throughout a person's lifetime. Developmental disabilities include autism, attention-deficit hyperactivity disorder (ADHD), cerebral palsy, and impairments of hearing and sight. People with developmental disabilities are more likely to have physical impairments, learning difficulties, language problems and behavioural problems (24).

Between 20% and 70% of people on the autism spectrum are believed to also have ADHD (25, 26). As the name suggests, individuals with ADHD have a short attention span and may be easily distracted. They may also be impulsive or restless, with constant fidgeting or over-activity.

Mental health

The term 'mental health problem' covers a wide range of psychological problems which affect someone's ability to get on with their daily life. Many individuals on the autism spectrum have one or more mental health problems.

For example, people with autism are also at increased risk of developing anxiety, depression, obsessive compulsive disorder and oppositional defiant disorder. Between 42% and 56% of people with autism will develop anxiety, and this is likely across all ages. Between 12% and 70% of people with autism will suffer from depression, and this is more likely in adults than it is in children. Between seven per cent and 24% of people with autism will develop an obsessive compulsive disorder. However, it is important to distinguish between obsessive compulsive disorders which involve intrusive anxiety-causing thoughts and between special interests, a part of autism which brings pleasure and happiness. Between 16% and 28% of people with autism will develop an oppositional defiant disorder, which could be due to rigid patterns of behaviour, difficulty seeing other points of view or anxiety (27).

Challenging behaviours

Challenging behaviour can be defined as: 'Culturally abnormal behaviour(s) of such intensity, frequency or duration that the physical safety of the person or others is placed in serious jeopardy, or behaviour which is likely to seriously limit or deny access to the use of ordinary community facilities' (28). Challenging behaviour can be directed to others, to self, to property and can include socially unacceptable behaviour.

Other examples of behaviour which could be considered challenging are physical and verbal aggression, absconding and inappropriate sexualised behaviour. Defining challenging behaviour can be subjective, as it does depend to some extent on a person's tolerance (for example, swearing may be seen as challenging to some while others do not mind it at all).

In the past challenging behaviour was considered to be 'a part of autism', but it has become increasingly clear that challenging behaviour serves a purpose. The underlying reasons for why a behaviour is occurring can be complex and difficult to understand (29) but trying to understand the underlying purpose of a behaviour can help to reduce the likelihood of it occurring and help to manage it when it does occur. Reasons why a behaviour may occur include problems with communication, issues with diet, inability to communicate pain appropriately, boredom, changes in routine, sensory issues, delays in processing information, anxiety, physical and mental illness.

Inclusion and exclusion

Inclusion means a wide range of things. It can mean being 'accepted by other people', 'taking part in community life', 'able to lead an independent life'. Or it can mean 'able to lead as normal a life as possible', 'included in the workplace', 'included in social/recreational activities' and 'offered the same opportunities as others'.

Unfortunately many people on the autism spectrum are routinely excluded from society and prevented from undertaking these activities (30).

For example, a report by the National Autistic Society stated that: 'People with autism and Asperger syndrome find it difficult interacting with others and making friends. As a result, many find themselves excluded socially. Almost a third (31%) of adults with autism or Asperger syndrome are involved in no social activities at all. This was higher for those in their teens and those with Asperger syndrome, both at 37%.

'The survey of more able adults found that over a third go out only 'rarely' to any social event, and half will only go out once or twice a month. Parents confirmed this: 82% said their son or daughter has difficulty taking part in social activities. This figure was even higher for those in their teens and 20s.' (30)

Impact on family

Autism doesn't just affect the person with the diagnosis; it also affects everybody else in the immediate family.

Some people say that having a family member on the autism spectrum is the best thing that has happened to the family.

> 'I feel privileged that my son is autistic because it has opened up a whole new world and made me look at everything so differently.' Parent (31)

However, some people say that they face a range of difficulties because a family member is autistic. For example, many of them become worried and exhausted looking after someone with autism. They also face the frustration of trying to find accurate information about interventions which work, discovering very little is currently known about most interventions, and of trying to cope with the lack of adequate services.

> 'People don't understand, they don't live with it 24 hours a day and get the constraints that come with him – I can't take him to Asda, can't take him on holiday because he can't stand the cabin pressure. It governs absolutely everything, where you go, what you eat, it's your whole life, even down to whether the patterns on the wallpaper are going to upset him. I can't do the simplest things that other people take for granted.' Parent of seven-year-old boy with autism (32)

In some cases these difficulties can lead to family breakdown. In others they can lead to the family becoming more resilient and more united.

Guidance for specific issues

We are giving you the best summary of different interventions that we can. We don't try to tell you which interventions to use to help an individual on the autism spectrum deal with a specific challenge or problem. However, the National Institute for Health and Care Excellence does provide guidance on which interventions may be most appropriate for some of the most common challenges and problems including: core symptoms, challenging behaviours, associated problems and affect on the family (see page 308). The Research Autism website also provides more information about specific issues with links to significant peer-reviewed research studies.

As Temple Grandin, a woman with autism says, there is no one-size-fits-all solution to the issues faced by people with autism. What works for one person may not work for another.

> 'People are always looking for the single magic bullet that will totally change everything. There is no single magic bullet.'
> Temple Grandin

References

1. White SW, Oswald D, Ollendick T & Scahill L (2009) Anxiety in children and adolescents with autism spectrum disorders. *Clinical Psychology Review* **29** 216–29.

2. Mazurek MO, Vasa RA, Kalb LG, Kanne SM, Rosenburg D, Keefer A, Murray DS, Freedman B & Lowery LA (2013) Anxiety, sensory over-responsivity, and gastrointestinal problems in children with autism spectrum disorders. *Journal of Abnormal Child Psychology* **41** 165–176.

3. FreeDictionary.com (2009) *Cognition*. Huntington Valley, PA: Farlex.

4. Rajendran G & Mitchell P (2007) Cognitive theories of autism. *Developmental Review* **27** 224–260.

5. Hill EL (2004) Executive dysfunction in autism. *Trends in Cognitive Sciences* **8** 26–32.

6. Frith U, Morton J & Leslie AM (1991) The cognitive basis of a biological disorder: autism. *Trends in Neurosciences* **14** 433–438.

7. Joseph R, Tager-Flusberg H & Lord C (2002) Cognitive profiles and social communicative functioning in children with autism spectrum disorder. *Journal of Child Psychology and Psychiatry* **43** 807–821.

8. Boucher J, Mayes A & Bigham S (2012) Memory in autistic spectrum disorder. *Psychological Bulletin* **138** 458–496.

9. Research Autism (2014) *Intellectual ability and autism* [online]. Available at: www.researchautism.net/intellectual-ability (accessed January 13, 2015).

10. Dictionary.com (2014) *Motor skills* [online]. Oakland, CA: Dictionary.com.

11. Gowen E & Hamilton A (2013) Motor abilities in autism: a review using a computational context. *Journal of Autism and Developmental Disorders* **43** 323–344.

12. Marco EJ, Hinkley LBN, Hill SS & Nagarajan SS (2011) Sensory processing in autism: a review of neurophysiologic findings. *Pediatric Research* **69** 48R–54R.

13. Attwood T (2007) Sensory Sensitivity. In: T Attwood *The Complete Guide to Asperger's Syndrome* (pp 271–291). London: Jessica Kingsley Publishers.

14. National Institute for Health and Care Excellence (2012) *Autism: Recognition, referral, diagnosis and management of adults on the autism spectrum*. London: National Institute for Health and Care Excellence.

15. Sarris M (2014) *Daily Living Skills: A key to independence for people with autism*. Baltimore, MD: IAN Network.

16. Kotagal S & Broomall E (2012) Sleep in children with autism spectrum disorder. *Pediatric Neurology* **47** 242–251.

17. Richdale AL & Schreck KA (2009) Sleep problems in autism spectrum disorders: prevalence, nature, & possible biopsychosocial aetiologies. *Sleep Medicine Reviews* **13** 403–411.

18. Glickman G (2010) Circadian rhythms and sleep in children with autism. *Neuroscience and Biobehavioral Reviews* **34** 755–768.

19. Hollway JA & Aman MG (2011) Sleep correlates of pervasive developmental disorders: a review of the literature. *Research in Developmental Disabilities* **32** 1399–1421.

20. Hagerman RJ (2007) *Fragile X Syndrome: A genetical model for autism with targeted treatments*. Baltimore, MD: IAN Network.

21. IAN Network (2010) *Tuberous Sclerosis*. Baltimore, MD: IAN Network.

22. Matson JL & Neal D (2009) Seizures and epilepsy and their relationship to autism spectrum disorders. *Research in Autism Spectrum Disorders* **3** 999–1005.

23. Buie T *et al* (2010) Evaluation, diagnosis, and treatment of gastrointestinal disorders in individuals with ASDs: a consensus report. *Pediatrics* doi:10.1542.

24. Center for Disease Control and Prevention (2013) *Facts about Developmental Disabilities*. Atlanta, GA: CDC.

25. Mannion A & Leader G (2014) Attention-deficit/hyperactivity disorder (AD/HD) in autism spectrum disorder. *Research in Autism Spectrum Disorders* **8** 432–439.

26. Matson JL, Rieske RD & Williams LW (2013) The relationship between autism spectrum disorders and attention-deficit/hyperactivity disorder: an overview. *Research in Developmental Disabilities* **34** 2475–2484.

27. Lai M-C, Lombardo MV & Baron-Cohen S (2014) Autism. *Lancet* **383** 896–910.

28. Emerson E (1995) *Challenging Behaviour: Analysis and intervention with people with severe learning difficulties*. Cambridge University Press, Cambridge.

29. Matson JL *et al* (2010) What is the evidence for environmental causes of challenging behaviors in persons with intellectual disabilities and autism spectrum disorders? *Research in Developmental Disabilities* **32** 693–8.

30. Barnard J, Harvey V, Potter D & Prior A (2001) *Ignored or Ineligible? The reality for adults with autism spectrum disorders*. London: National Autistic Society.

31. Myers BJ, Mackintosh VH & Goin-Kochel RP (2009) My greatest joy and my greatest heart ache: parents' own words on how having a child in the autism spectrum has affected their lives and their families' lives. *Research in Autism Spectrum Disorders* **3** 670–684.

32. Simmons L (2007) *Think Differently: Act positively*. London: National Autistic Society.

Chapter 3:
Interventions

Introduction

Here we present a summary of the different types of intervention used to help people on the autism spectrum, and the purposes of different interventions. We discuss some of the practical difficulties with interventions (such as the difficulty of designing interventions for such a diverse group of people).

Later in the book we look at the interventions in more detail. We give each type of intervention its own chapter, and examine specific examples of that type of intervention, along with the claims and evidence behind them. We also look at practical issues such as the supply and regulation of these interventions, the time and cost required to use them, and their safety and risk.

Definitions

We define an intervention as any action (such as a treatment or therapy or the provision of a service) which is designed to help people on the autism spectrum (or their parents and carers) (1).

> 'To intervene is to stop something from happening: to prevent or alter a course of events. In the world of autism I believe we must intervene very carefully because to intervene can easily become an act of sabotaging who a person really is.' (2)

Types of intervention

The hundreds of interventions available have no universally agreed system of classification. We have adopted what we hope is a practical approach, grouping similar interventions together into categories that make sense to us. However we acknowledge that some people would put different interventions into different categories.

'One simple test for anybody thinking about using a particular type of intervention on autistic people is whether you would be happy if autistic people, or anyone else, were to use the same intervention on you.' (3)

We have grouped interventions as follows:

- standard healthcare – such as occupational therapy
- complementary and alternative medicine
  – such as homeopathy
- alternative and augmentative communication
  – such as sign language
- assistive and adaptive technology
  – such as computer apps
- behavioural and developmental interventions
  – such as positive behaviour support
- medications
  – such as risperidone
- diets and dietary supplements
  – such as omega-3 fatty acid supplements
- alternative medical procedures
  – such as chelation
- motor-sensory interventions
  – such as sensory integrative therapy
- psychological interventions
  – such as cognitive behavioural therapy
- social care services
  – such as supported living
- vocational interventions
  – such as supported employment
- animal-assisted activities and therapies
  – such as assistance dogs.

Please remember that some interventions can be placed in a number of different categories. For example, cognitive behavioural therapy (CBT) can be classed as a psychosocial intervention and as a form of behavioural therapy.

Purpose

The interventions that people choose are influenced by their understanding of what autism is. The wide range of available interventions reflects the diverse theories and ideas about what causes autism and the underlying cognitive differences.

> 'The treatment often has more to do with the belief system of the therapist than the needs of the child.' (4)

An important question to ask about any intervention is 'what is it trying to achieve?'

In general, interventions are designed to do one or more of the following things:

1. **Cure autism.** Autism is a lifelong condition so interventions that claim to cure autism don't have any reliable scientific evidence. However, some research is more nuanced. Instead of talking of cures, it talks of recovery and 'optimal outcomes', especially in relation to early intervention. Some proponents of early intervention describe a specific group of children who later lose their diagnosis (optimal outcome). However, the reality is much more complicated.

2. **Target the core difficulties in autism.** For example, social skills, communication skills or restrictive and repetitive behaviours. These interventions usually aim to help a person to learn to adapt to the world around them.

3. **Reduce challenging behaviour.** These interventions aim to reduce the incidence of self-harm, aggression and other challenging behaviours. One of the difficulties with this is the way that challenging behaviour is viewed and defined. Often, it is defined too broadly, and can be mistaken for behaviour which is challenging to the person working with the person with autism. For example, a person rocking in the corner could be doing this because they enjoy this and find it comforting. On the other hand, it could signal that the person is in pain. It is important to know the individual to understand whether a behaviour is challenging or not.

4. **Treating co-existing conditions such as epilepsy or gastrointestinal problems.** These interventions are not designed to help with the autism itself but instead aim to treat co-occurring conditions.
5. **Improve the quality of life of the person with autism (or their parents, siblings and carers).** This can be using social skills interventions or providing assistance to find employment (1).

Challenges to choosing an intervention

With all the interventions available, how can you know which interventions actually work? Most interventions do appear to produce some benefits, otherwise people wouldn't use them (1). However, these effects may not be long-lasting, may be weak or may not be real. Several challenges face those choosing an intervention:

The complexity of autism and the individuality of people on the spectrum

An intervention which can target all the aspects highlighted above is likely never to be possible due to the complexity of autism and the fact that every person on the autism spectrum is different. An intervention that can target every person with autism is also unlikely.

Supply and availability

The availability of an intervention depends on where you live and whether it is offered by the local authority. Some people choose to go private, and some choose to travel quite a distance for an intervention, but others may not be able to afford this.

Cost and time

Some interventions are extremely expensive and require many hours of work each week over many years. Furthermore, many families choose a number of interventions to do at the same time, which can further affect the amount of time and money spent.

Risks and safety

Some interventions carry risks, which are important to consider when choosing an intervention.

Family circumstance

Some interventions can affect the family due to the financial and emotional costs.

Evidence

At the moment, not many interventions have robust scientific research into their effectiveness. Probably the most researched interventions are behavioural, such as ABA. As we will see, research into ABA is complicated by the wide variety of different methods which claim to be based on ABA. So it's very difficult to compare interventions and this makes doing quality research very difficult. At the other end of the scale, very little research on interventions for adults exists. However, the research that does exist gives us some idea of which interventions are promising (5–7).

We have a more detailed look at how interventions are evaluated in Chapter 4 – see page 43.

References

1. Research Autism (2013) Introduction to interventions for autism [online]. Available at: www.researchautism.net/introduction-autism-interventions (accessed January 13, 2015).

2. Yorke A (2014) Personal correspondence with Autism West Midlands.

3. Milton D (2013) Personal correspondence with Research Autism.

4. Wing L (1977) *Dr Lorna Wing, OBE* [online]. Available at: www.researchautism.net/lorna-wing (accessed January 26, 2015).

5. Pellicano L, Dinsmore A & Charman T (2013) *A Future Made Together*. London: Institute of Education.

6. National Institute for Health and Care Excellence (2012) *Autism: Recognition, referral, diagnosis and management of adults on the autism spectrum*. London: National Institute for Health and Care Excellence.

7. National Institute for Health and Care Excellence (2013) *The Management and Support of Children and Young People on the Autism Spectrum*. London: National Institute for Health and Care Excellence.

Chapter 4:
Evaluating interventions

Introduction

We want to help you understand how scientists evaluate interventions, so in this chapter we examine the research process, and describe its strengths and weaknesses. We look at the different types of research study and explain why some studies are more scientifically robust than others. We describe some of the key sources of research evidence and look at some of the different systems used by researchers to evaluate that evidence.

The research process

We use this definition of research: 'the systematic investigation into and study of materials and sources in order to establish facts and reach new conclusions' (1). Good research is a dynamic process which tries to answer questions systematically and evolves in response to the results of previous experiments (2). It starts with a hypothesis – an idea which would provide a solution to a problem – such as how to reduce anxiety in someone on the autism spectrum.

Predictions are made on what you should see if the hypothesis is correct and experiments are designed to test the idea. If the results of the experiments support the hypothesis, this does not automatically mean that the hypothesis is accurate. More experiments are needed to be sure that the results can be reproduced by other research groups that are independent.

If the results do not support the hypothesis, it should either be modified and tested again or discarded altogether. This process is what makes the research process strong. Even if an explanation sounds plausible and convincing, it is not accepted as a valid theory until it has been tested multiple times. Alternative explanations are also considered and tested by other research groups (2).

Figure 4.1: The research process

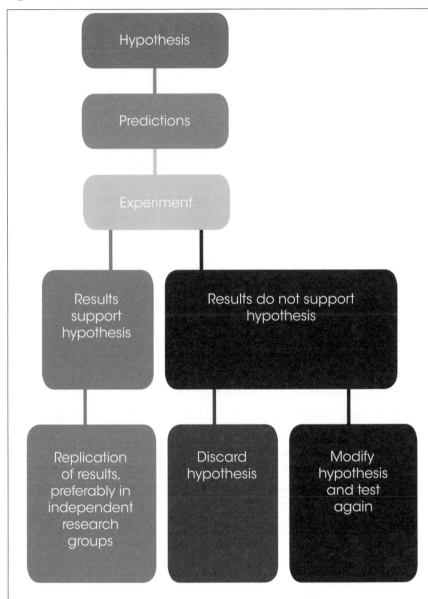

Figure first published in *The Good and The Bad Science of Autism* (2012) by Walsh and Hurley (2). Reproduced with permission from Autism West Midlands

After the research study is finished

Once a research study is completed, it is submitted for publication in a peer-reviewed journal. This means that before it can be published it must be reviewed anonymously, usually by other experts in the field. These experts will make comments on the research and the results and may require that the author provides more information or performs more analysis before it is published. They can also decide that the article is not suitable for their journal and reject it altogether. The peer-review process is not perfect and articles with flaws will be published. However, these can then be evaluated by the wider scientific community. Other researchers may publish articles with different results and it can be years before there is a general agreement within the scientific community on a particular subject. Very often the answer is more complex than a simple 'yes' or 'no' and this explains why the scientific process can take such a long time.

Limitations to the research process

Although research can take a long time to get answers, the process itself has many strengths, as it is objective, it changes when new evidence comes along and the peer-review process provides a way of criticising the research before it is published. There are, however, a number of limitations to this approach.

1. **People on the autism spectrum are very different from each other**

    In autism research this causes a bit of a problem as trying to look at the effect of an intervention on a group which is made up of very different people is difficult. It is likely that they will all respond differently so the overall effect may be small. However, some people within the group may respond very positively while others may not respond at all. For this reason, there is some discussion about how to identify different groups of people with autism who may respond to things in similar ways. This would allow for bigger effects of interventions in research but will also help people to better identify interventions that would be suitable for them.

2. The way that research is reported has limitations

Unfortunately, it is common for research studies to report only positive data as this makes it easier for researchers to obtain more funding for future work. This means that there can be missing information on the side effects of an intervention, for example. Furthermore, in the early stages of research on a particular intervention, it is likely that most findings will be positive due to this bias towards publishing only positive results. It can take years before research showing that an intervention is less effective than previously thought is published (3).

3. Research does not always address real world implications

Another important limitation to research is how it addresses real-world implications. First of all, many research studies look at very specific methods for their interventions and it is likely that in the real world practitioners may not stick to these methods exactly (this could be due to it being impractical to follow all the methods exactly). The evidence base would be for the exact methods used in the research so real-world interventions may not have the same level of evidence. Secondly, there is a lot of research which addresses theoretical ideas as opposed to real-world questions such as improving quality of life. Although researching theoretical constructs is important to improve our general understanding of autism, recent research has identified that the people directly affected by research want to see more research which has real-life implications (4). This has important implications for how researchers view the significance of results. Researchers should consider what would be considered significant in the real world: is an intervention significant if the outcome is only 20 minutes' extra sleep but the intervention costs a lot of money? If an intervention causes a lot of family stress and a strain on income, are any improvements seen worth this?

4. Research does not always involve people on the autism spectrum

Most of the research conducted to date has not included people on the autism spectrum or their families in any meaningful sense. For example, most research about autism tends to include people on the autism spectrum and their families as subjects rather than as part of the research team. Where autistic people or their families are included on the research team, they tend to be included as advisors rather than as actual researchers. This led Milton to comment:

'I argue that autistic people have often become distrustful of researchers and their aims, and are frequently frozen out of the processes of knowledge production. Such a context results in a negative feedback spiral with further damage to the growth of interactional expertise between researchers and autistic people, and a breakdown in trust and communication leading to an increase in tension between stakeholder groups' (5).

In the recent report on autism research, *A Future Made Together* (2013), an important point that was made was that there is still not enough research on interventions compared to other areas of autism (4). However, it was seen as a priority for many parents, people with autism and practitioners that research should focus on improving quality of life in people with autism. It will be important for the research community to respond to this research and shape their research priorities based on the needs of those directly affected by autism.

Types of research study

Randomised controlled trials

The 'gold standard' in research is the randomised, controlled trial (RCT) which is a study designed to be as scientifically rigorous as possible. A good RCT includes the following elements:

1. Controlled

A controlled study compares a group that receives the

experimental treatment to a group that receives no treatment or a standard treatment (the control group). In some studies, the control group is given a placebo to reduce the likelihood that people could guess which group they are in. For example, in medical trials, a person may either be given a pill which contains active ingredients or a sugar pill that looks identical to the active pill, but does not contain any active ingredients. This means the only difference between the two groups is whether they are given active ingredients or not.

2. Randomised

When a study is randomised, the participants are randomly put into either the treatment group or the control group. No one is able to influence who is put in a group, and this reduces the risk of selection bias. Selection bias is when participants are chosen for the treatment group that are more likely to respond. This can make a treatment seem more effective than it is.

3. Blinded

In a research study, blinding refers to when people do not know which is the control group and which is the treatment group. A single-blinded study means that the participants do not know which group they are in, but the researchers do know. A double-blinded study means that neither the participants nor the researchers know which group they are in. Open label means that the study is not blinded in any way.

4. Statistically significant

If a treatment has a statistically significant effect, this means that the likelihood that the effect was due to chance is less than five per cent. However, it is important to note that a statistically significant result may not always be completely accurate. The number of participants used in a study will influence the level of significance. Statistically significant results found in small studies are often not replicated in larger studies as the small number of people might not be as typical a group as a large number. A large number will average out any accidental differences. The ideal research study would have a large number of participants. Furthermore, it is important for researchers to use the correct statistical tests, as some tests are more likely to produce significant results than others.

In practice, most published research studies do not meet these rigorous standards for a variety of reasons. For example, large, randomised, controlled trials are very costly to set up, to run and to evaluate.

It is more sensible to carry out small, cheap, less rigorous studies to test the hypothesis before planning larger studies. Many other types of research study are not as rigorous as an RCT. However each type of study can provide valuable information which may then pave the way to finding a good hypothesis through an RCT.

Case study

A case study is a study which reports observations on a single individual. So, for example, a case study might report on a child with autism who was given the drug risperidone. Case studies are considered to be low-quality because the risk of bias is significantly higher than in most other types of study, mainly because they only look at one individual.

Case series

A case series is a study which reports observations on a series of individuals, usually all receiving the same intervention. So, for example, a case series might report on three children with autism who received risperidone. Case series are considered to be higher quality than case studies because they report on more than one individual but the risk of bias is still very high.

Multiple-baseline design

A multiple-baseline design is a study that measures several things before and after an intervention in order to see whether the intervention had any effect on those things. So, for example, it might look at whether an intervention reduces anxiety and improves social interaction in three people on the autism spectrum. Multiple baseline studies are considered to be higher quality than case series because they set out to examine a specific hypothesis and because they carefully measure a number of different things before and after the intervention.

Qualitative research studies

Qualitative research studies do not focus on making measurements but instead analyse the answers that participants give to broad questions and identify themes and patterns in the answers. For example, a researcher might want to know about sibling relationships. A qualitative research study would ask siblings about their experiences with their brother or sister with autism. The researcher could then extract themes such as 'protectiveness', 'acceptance' and 'compassion'. The strength of qualitative research is generally the depth of insight and information which it can reveal and which can increase our understanding of the issues under investigation. Qualitative research can provide a more personalised and a more realistic view of the lives of people on the autism spectrum (6).

Published sources of evidence

Published sources of evidence are resources which assess the evidence for the effectiveness of autism interventions. They include but are not limited to research reviews, clinical guidance and best practice statements.

Please note: we cannot list every source of evidence in a book of this size, so we have tried to highlight some of the most important or representative sources. The fact that we have listed a source does not necessarily mean that we agree with what it says.

Research reviews

A number of autism organisations/websites have published research reviews on interventions used to support people on the autism spectrum. These research reviews are designed to examine and evaluate the scientific research evidence on specific topics.

- Association for Science in Autism Treatment at www. asatonline.org
- National Autism Center at www.nationalautismcenter.org
- National Professional Development Center on Autism Spectrum Disorders at http://autismpdc.fpg.unc.edu/
- Research Autism at www.researchautism.net

A number of other organisations/websites have published research reviews on a wide range of interventions, including some on autism:

- Agency for Healthcare Research and Quality at www.ahrq.gov
- Cochrane Collaboration at www.cochrane.org
- PubMed at www.ncbi.nlm.nih.gov/pubmed (7, 8, 9)

Clinical guidance

A number of organisations have published clinical guidance on the management and support of people on the autism spectrum. These guidance documents are designed to inform policy and practice, that is, they are designed to change how services are actually delivered on the ground.

In the UK, the most important of these organisations is the National Institute for Health and Care Excellence (NICE) at www.nice.org.uk, which has published a number of key guidance documents on adults and on children and young people (10, 11).

We have included a summary of the key NICE guidance on page 308 of this book.

Best practice statements

A number of professional associations have published best practice statements on the management and support of people on the autism spectrum. These statements are designed to update members and other people on best practice on specific issues.

For example, in the UK, the Royal College of Speech and Language Therapists has published guidance on reasonable adjustments to communication that individuals with learning disabilities and/or autism should expect in specialist hospital and residential settings (12).

In the US, the American Occupational Therapy Association has published guidance on helping students with autism achieve greater success in academic performance and social participation (13).

Evaluation systems

There are a number of evaluation systems used by researchers to provide guidance on interventions. Each system has its advantages and disadvantages but they are all designed to do the same job: to show you the level of evidence for or against specific interventions.

GRADE

The GRADE system (Grades of Recommendation, Assessment, Development and Evaluation) is used by a range of national and international professional medical societies, health-related branches of government, and healthcare regulatory bodies including the National Institute for Health and Care Excellence (NICE) in the UK.

GRADE has numerous advantages including the fact that it is extremely rigorous and widely accepted by the scientific community.

The main disadvantage of the GRADE system is that it excludes most research studies. It only includes studies which are randomised controlled trials (14).

NPDC

The National Professional Development Center on Autism Spectrum Disorders (NPDC) has developed a system for evaluating interventions which is used by a number of academic researchers, especially in the USA. The NPDC system includes quasi-experimental studies and small, single case design studies, as well as randomised controlled trials.

The main advantage of the NPDC system is that it includes a much wider range of research studies than the GRADE system. The main disadvantage of the NPDC system is that it includes some lower quality studies (7).

Research Autism

The Research Autism website uses a system which sits halfway between the GRADE system and the NPDC system. For example, it includes quasi-experimental studies but does not include small, single case design studies.

The main advantages of the Research Autism system are that it includes and evaluates a much wider range of studies than would be included using the GRADE system but does not include some of the very small scale studies that would be included using the NPDC system (15).

Because each evaluation system uses different criteria to judge the same studies they may produce different results. For example, under the NPDC system, some interventions are accepted as evidence-based practices but they are not accepted as evidence-based practices under the GRADE system or the Research Autism system.

This book

This book uses a system based on the Research Autism website system. See Appendix 3, page 330, for more information on our evidence levels.

References

1. The Oxford English Dictionary (2013). Research [online]. Available at: www.oxforddictionaries.com/definition/english/research (accessed 27 January, 2015).

2. Walsh N & Hurley E (2013) *The Good and Bad Science of Autism*. Autism West Midlands, Birmingham. pp 6–11.

3. Research Autism (2014) *Why some autism research studies are flawed* [online]. Available at: www.researchautism.net/research-study-flaws (accessed January 13, 2015).

4. Pellicano L, Dinsmore A & Charman T (2013) *A Future Made Together*. London: Institute of Education.

5. Milton DE (2014) Autistic expertise: a critical reflection on the production of knowledge in autism studies. *Autism* **17** (8) 794–802.

6. Research Autism (2014) *Types of autism research study* [online]. Available at: www.researchautism.net/research-study-types (accessed January 13, 2015).

7. Wong C, Odom SL, Hume K, Cox AW, Fettig A, Kucharczyk S, Brock ME, Plavnick, JB, Fleury VP & Schultz TR (2013) *Evidence-based Practices for Children, Youth, and Young Adults with Autism Spectrum Disorder*. Chapel Hill, NC: The University of North Carolina.

8. Agency for Healthcare Research (2012) *Therapies for Children with Autism Spectrum Disorders*. Rockville, MD: Agency for Healthcare Research and Quality.

9. Agency for Healthcare Research and Quality (2012) *Interventions for Adolescents and Young Adults with Autism Spectrum Disorders*. Rockville, MD: Agency for Healthcare Research and Quality.

10. National Institute for Health and Care Excellence (2012) *Autism: Recognition, referral, diagnosis and management of adults on the autism spectrum*. London: National Institute for Health and Care Excellence.

11. National Institute for Health and Care Excellence (2013) *The Management and Support of Children and Young People on the Autism Spectrum*. London: National Institute for Health and Care Excellence.

12. Royal College of Speech and Language Therapists (2013) *Five Good Communication Standards: Reasonable adjustments to communication that individuals with learning disability and/or autism should expect in specialist hospital and residential settings*. London: Royal College of Speech and Language Therapists.

13. American Occupational Therapy Association (2009) *Help Students with Autism Achieve Greater Success in Academic Performance and*

Social Participation. Bethesda: MD: American Occupational Therapy Association.

14. GRADE Working Group (2015) Welcome [online]. Available at: www. gradeworkinggroup.org/index.htm (accessed January 27 2015).

15. Research Autism (2014) *Ratings of treatment studies for autism*. [online]. Available at: www.researchautism.net/our-ratings-system(accessed January 13, 2015).

Section 2
Interventions

Introduction

The chapters in this section provide details about the different types of interventions, along with an evaluation of the evidence base behind each intervention. The chapters also provide information about the cost and time required to undertake the intervention, the supply and regulation (quality control) of the intervention, and any risks.

Chapter 5:

Standard healthcare

Introduction

Standard healthcare (aka conventional medicine, mainstream medicine or allopathic medicine) is a system of healthcare based on the 'Western model' of evidence-based practice for diagnosing and treating conditions.

A wide range of approaches are part of standard healthcare, all of them accepted and used by a large majority of healthcare professionals in the UK and other Western countries.

Standard healthcare includes many different disciplines including art therapies, diets, medication, medical procedures, occupational therapy, osteopathy, physiotherapy, psychology, psychotherapy, and speech and language therapy (1, 2).

In practice, standard healthcare staff often work as part of a team with other healthcare providers (and sometimes teachers and parents) to provide a package of care designed to meet the needs of the individual.

Standard healthcare is used to treat an enormous range of conditions (such as cancer, depression and stroke). Some standard healthcare practices are also being used to treat some of the problems faced by people on the autism spectrum, including the core symptoms of autism (such as difficulties with social interaction) and some of the associated problems (such as anxiety) (3, 4).

The hypotheses behind different standard healthcare practices vary from one practice to another. For example, physiotherapy is based on the idea that human movement is central to the health and well-being of individuals. Psychology, on the other hand, is concerned with all aspects of behaviour and with the thoughts, feelings and motivations underlying that behaviour.

Evidence

The scientific evidence for the use of the various forms of standard healthcare to help individuals on the autism spectrum varies enormously from one form of standard healthcare to another. For example, the evidence base for the use of psychological practices and medication is considerably stronger than the evidence base for the use of diets (3–6).

NICE guidelines

No firm recommendations on standard healthcare practices (such as occupational therapy) have been made by the National Institute for Health and Care Excellence.

Supply, quality and regulation

The availability of standard healthcare varies enormously from country to country and even within the same country. For example, in the UK, some therapies (such as cognitive behavioural therapy) may be available to some people on the autism spectrum on the NHS or through a school but not to others, depending on where they live. However, paying privately is often possible for most forms of standard healthcare.

The credentials required for standard health practitioners vary tremendously from country to country. For example, in the UK, GPs and psychiatrists are regulated by the General Medical Council, and allied healthcare professionals are regulated by the Health and Care Professions Council (7).

Costs and time

Costs: in the UK, most standard healthcare provided on the NHS is free of charge. However, paying privately is usually possible for some forms of standard healthcare. The actual cost may depend on a number of factors including: the type and complexity of your case, the level of experience and specialist expertise of the therapist, and the type of service that is being offered.

Time: the length of treatment may vary depending on a number of things, including the specific form of healthcare, the individual practitioner, and the needs of the individual on the autism spectrum. Those with more serious or ongoing problems may take longer to help, perhaps months or years.

Risks and safety

The risks from standard healthcare vary enormously from one type of healthcare practice to another. For example, some medications may cause significant side effects whereas speech and language therapy is unlikely to cause any significant side effects (8).

Specific forms of standard healthcare

Arts therapies

Please see Chapter 22 for our detailed entry on psychological therapies on page 238.

Diets

Please see Chapters 18 and 19 for our detailed entries on diets and supplements on pages 194 and 205.

Medications

Please see Chapter 17 for our detailed entry on medications on page 168.

Medical procedures

Please see Chapter 20 for our detailed entry on alternative medical procedures on page 219.

Occupational therapy

Introduction

Occupational therapy uses specific, purposeful activity (such as assembling hospital records folders) to assess, prevent and treat physical and psychiatric conditions to prevent disability and promote independent function in all aspects of daily life.

In practice, occupational therapy may be used to help an individual with autism to achieve and maintain normal daily tasks such as getting dressed, engaging in social interactions, completing school activities, and working or playing.

> ## Occupational therapy
>
> **Definition:** therapy which assesses and treats conditions using specific, purposeful activity to promote independent function.
>
> **Aims:** to promote independent functioning in individuals with autism.
>
> **Who:** people with autism, including children and adults.
>
> **Evidence:** assessing possible benefits is difficult due to the wide range of practices.
>
> **Risks:** no significant risks.

The occupational therapist may use a wide range of different interventions, techniques and tools. For example, they may create games which help the individual to socialise with other people, or use sensory techniques to help the individual process sensory information more effectively, or help the individual to find and use the right kind of computer software (9).

Aims

Various claims have been made for the role of occupational therapy and also for some of the specific techniques and approaches used by some occupational therapists when treating people on the autism spectrum. For example, the College of Occupational Therapy reported that:

'Evidence shows that by working collaboratively with the child and the family to identify and achieve their goals, occupational therapists enable children with ASD to participate more fully in everyday life, reduce parental stress and increase feelings of confident parenting.' (10)

Evidence

Determining the benefits of occupational therapy for individuals on the autism spectrum is difficult because it includes such a wide range of practices, each of which has different levels of research evidence (11).

Risks and safety

No significant risks are associated with occupational therapy.

Physiotherapy
Introduction

Physiotherapy (known as physical therapy in the US) is based on the idea that human movement is central to the health and well-being of individuals.

In practice, physiotherapists may use a wide range of techniques and strategies to help an individual with autism get the most out of his or her movement.

For example, they may work on basic movement skills, such as sitting, standing and playing. They may also work on more complex skills such as kicking, throwing and catching (12, 13).

Physiotherapy

Definition: therapy which uses a range of techniques and strategies to help an individual get the most out of their movement.

Aims: to help individuals with autism get the most out of movement.

Who: people with autism, including children and adults.

Evidence: assessing possible benefits is difficult due to the wide range of practices.

Risks: minor risks associated with movement.

Aims

Various claims have been made for physiotherapy, and also for some of the specific techniques and approaches used by some physiotherapists when treating people on the autism spectrum.

For example, a review of the use of vigorous physical exercise in people with ASD found that exercise interventions may decrease 'stereotypy, aggression, off-task behaviour and elopement' (14).

Evidence

Determining the benefits of physiotherapy for individuals on the autism spectrum is difficult because it includes such a wide range of practices, each of which has different levels of research evidence (15).

Risks and safety

Some minor risks are associated with some of the activities undertaken by some physiotherapists, such as minor sprains or bruises following physical activities.

Psychiatry

Introduction

Psychiatry is concerned with the diagnosis, treatment and prevention of mental health problems.

Mental health problems that may be diagnosed and treated by a psychiatrist include: anxiety, phobias, obsessive compulsive disorder, depression, eating disorders and sleep disorders.

The psychiatrist may use a wide range of different interventions, techniques and tools. For example, they might prescribe antipsychotic medications or provide cognitive behaviour therapy to help someone overcome their anxiety (16).

Psychiatry

Definition: practice using a wide range of techniques and strategies to help an individual deal with mental health problems.

Aims: to help individuals with autism deal with a range of mental health problems.

Who: people with autism, including children and adults.

Evidence: assessing the possible benefits is difficult due to the wide range of practices.

Risks: specific forms of treatment, such as some medications, have some risks.

Choosing Autism Interventions: A Research-Based Guide © Research Autism and Autism West Midlands

Aims

Various claims have been made for the role of psychiatry and also for some of the specific techniques and approaches used by some psychiatrists when treating people on the autism spectrum.

For example, the Royal College of Psychiatrists claims that, while there are no known cures for autism, multidisciplinary teams (which often include psychiatrists) can help children and families in many ways. These include making a diagnosis, giving people information, managing behavioural difficulties, helping to develop social communication and emotional skills, treating co-occurring conditions, and using medication in some cases (17).

Evidence

Determining the benefits of psychiatry for individuals on the autism spectrum is difficult because it includes such a wide range of practices, each of which has different levels of research evidence (18).

Risks and safety

The risks will depend mostly on the specific methods being used by the psychiatrist. For example, some medications can cause significant and potentially hazardous side effects, whereas cognitive behavioural therapy is unlikely to carry significant risks (8).

Psychology

Introduction

Psychology is the scientific study of the human mind and behaviour: how we think, feel, act and interact, individually and in groups.

Psychology is concerned with all aspects of behaviour and with the thoughts, feelings and motivations underlying that behaviour.

In practice, psychologists help people with all sorts of problems, working with them to bring about change for the better. For example, a psychologist may help someone on the autism spectrum to deal with social interactions.

The therapist may use a wide range of different interventions, techniques and tools. For example, they may use many of the interventions described in Chapter 9 on behavioural and developmental interventions – page 105 – and Chapter 22 on psychological interventions – page 238. They may also work with a number of other professionals (such as teachers) and parents and carers (19).

> Psychology
>
> **Definition:** practices based on the scientific study of the human mind.
>
> **Aims:** to help individuals with autism with their core features and associated issues, such as anxiety.
>
> **Who:** people with autism, including children and adults.
>
> **Evidence:** assessing the possible benefits is difficult due to the wide range of practices.
>
> **Risks:** no significant risks.

Aims

Various claims have been made for the role of psychologists, and also for some of the specific techniques and approaches used by some psychologists when treating people on the autism spectrum.

For example, the Oxford Educational Assessment Centre claims that educational psychologists may be able to help with the assessment and treatment of issues such as significant difficulties with language development, significant difficulty in engaging in social interactions, an inconsistent response to sensory input, and a very restricted range of interests and activities which may be highly focused and repeated constantly (20).

Evidence

Determining the possible benefits of psychology for individuals on the autism spectrum is difficult because it includes such a wide range of practices, each of which has different levels of research evidence (6).

Risks and safety

No significant risks are associated with most psychological practices.

Psychological therapies

Please see Chapter 23 for our detailed entry on psychological therapies on page 238 and Chapter 9 on behavioural and developmental interventions – page 105.

Speech and language therapy

Introduction

Speech and language therapists work to assess, diagnose and develop a programme of care to maximise the communication skills of individuals who experience speech, language and other communication difficulties.

In practice, speech and language therapists do more than just teach an individual to speak. They may also teach someone how to understand and use a range of other skills, such as what non-verbal signals mean and how to take part in a two-way conversation.

> **Speech and language therapy**
>
> **Definition:** therapy which helps an individual to maximise their communication skills.
>
> **Aims:** to help individuals with autism who experience speech, language and other communication difficulties.
>
> **Who:** people with autism, including children and adults.
>
> **Evidence:** assessing the possible benefits is difficult due to the wide range of practices.
>
> **Risks:** no significant risks.

Speech and language therapists use a wide range of techniques and strategies. For example, they may teach non-verbal children how to use electronic devices or manual signing systems (21).

Aims

Various claims have been made for the role of speech and language therapy and also for some of the specific techniques and approaches used by some speech and language therapists when treating people on the autism spectrum. For example, the American Speech-Language-Hearing Association claims that speech and language therapists 'play a critical role in screening, diagnosing, and enhancing the social communication development and quality of life of children, adolescents, and adults with ASD' (22).

Evidence

Determining the possible benefits of speech and language therapy for individuals on the autism spectrum is difficult because it includes such a wide range of practices, each of which has different research evidence (23).

Risks and safety

No significant risks are associated with speech and language therapy.

Further information

In this book: Please see How to use this book (page 11), Chapter 3 (page 38) for information about interventions, Chapter 4 (page 43) for information about how scientists evaluate those interventions, and Section 3 (page 284) for advice on making the decision about whether or not to use a specific intervention.

Website: Please see www.researchautism.net/standard-health-care for information about standard healthcare including information about specific interventions and details of scientific studies and trials.

References

1. Medicinenet.com (2014) *Conventional medicine* [online]. New York, NY: Web MD.

2. FreeDictionary.com (2014) *Mainstream Medicine*. Huntington Valley, PA: Farlex.

3. National Institute for Health and Care Excellence (2012) *Autism: Recognition, referral, diagnosis and management of adults on the autism spectrum*. London: National Institute for Health and Care Excellence.

4. National Institute for Health and Care Excellence (2013) *The Management and Support of Children and Young People on the Autism Spectrum*. London: National Institute for Health and Care Excellence.

5. Research Autism (2014) *Medications and autism* [online]. Available at: http://www.researchautism.net/medications (accessed January 13, 2015).

6. Research Autism (2014) *Psychological interventions and autism* [online]. Available at: http://www.researchautism.net/psychological-interventions (accessed January 13, 2015).

7. General Medical Council. (2014) *UK Health and Social Care Regulators* [online]. Available at: www.gmc-uk.org/about/UK_health_and_social_care_regulators.asp (accessed January 13, 2015).

8. Politte LC *et al* (2014) Psychopharmacological interventions in autism spectrum disorder. *Harvard Review of Psychiatry* **22** (2) pp. 76–92.

9. NHS Choices (2012) *Occupational Therapy*. London, UK: NHS.

10. College of Occupational Therapists (2014) *Occupational Therapists Help Children and Young People with Autistic Spectrum Disorder to Participate in Everyday Tasks and Cope with Busy Environments*. London, UK: College of Occupational Therapists.

11. Research Autism (2014) *Occupational therapy and autism* [online]. Available at: www.researchautism.net/occupational-therapy-and-autism (accessed January 13, 2015).

12. Chartered Society of Physiotherapy (2013) *What is Physiotherapy?* London, UK: Chartered Society of Physiotherapy.

13. NHS Choices (2014) *Physiotherapy: How it works*. London, UK: NHS.

14. Lang R, Koegel LK, Ashbaugh K, Regester A, Ence W & Smith W (2010) Physical exercise and individuals with autism spectrum disorders: A systematic review. *Research in Autism Spectrum Disorders* **4** 565–576.

15. Research Autism (2014) *Physiotherapy and autism* [online]. Available at: www.researchautism.net/physiotherapy-and-autism (accessed January 13, 2015).

16. NHS Choices (2013) *Psychiatry*. London, UK: NHS.

17. Royal College of Psychiatrists (2012) *Autism and Asperger's Syndrome*. London, UK: Royal College of Psychiatrists.

18. Research Autism (2014) *Psychiatry* [online]. Available at: www.researchautism.net/psychiatry (accessed January 13, 2015).

19. British Psychological Society (2014) *Introduction to Psychology*. London, UK: British Psychological Society.

20. Oxford Educational Assessment Centre (2011) *Autism and Educational Psychology*. Oxford, UK: Oxford Educational Assessment Centre.

21. Royal College of Speech and Language Therapists (2014) *What is Speech and Language Therapy?* London, UK: Royal College of Speech and Language Therapists.

22. American Speech-Language-Hearing Association (2006) *Principles for Speech-Language Pathologists in Diagnosis, Assessment, and Treatment of Autism Spectrum Disorders Across the Life Span*. Rockville, MD: American Speech-Language-Hearing Association.

23. Research Autism (2014) *Speech and language therapy and autism* [online]. Available at: www.researchautism.net/speech-and-language-therapy-and-autism (accessed January 13, 2015).

Chapter 6:
Complementary and alternative medicine

Introduction

Complementary and alternative medicine (CAM) is a group of diverse medical and healthcare systems, practices, and products that are not generally considered part of conventional, Western medicine as practiced by medical doctors and allied health professionals.

'Complementary medicine' refers to the use of CAM together with conventional medicine. 'Alternative medicine' refers to the use of CAM in place of conventional medicine.

CAM practices are sometimes divided into two main sub-categories: natural products and mind-body medicine. However there are various other sub-categories including whole medical systems, manipulative and body-based practices, movement therapies, energy medicine and so on. In practice, many forms of CAM fall into more than one sub-category. For example, qigong massage can be categorised as mind-body medicine, as a manipulative or body-based practice, or as energy medicine (1, 2).

CAM practices (like standard healthcare practices) are used to treat a wide range of conditions (such as cancer, depression and stroke). Some CAM practices are also being used to treat some of the problems faced by people on the autism spectrum, including the core features of autism (such as difficulties with social interaction) and some of the associated problems (such as anxiety) (3–6).

The hypotheses behind different CAM practices vary from one practice to another, but practices within the sub-categories often share the same hypothesis. For example, practices based on energy medicine are all based on the idea of manipulating energy fields of one kind or another.

Evidence

The scientific evidence for the use of CAM practices to help individuals on the autism spectrum varies between different CAM practices.

In most cases, either no evidence exists at all or the evidence has no significance for making decisions about treatment; it just indicates the need for more research (7,8).

NICE guidelines

Insufficient evidence exists for making any firm recommendations on many specific CAM practices according to the National Institute for Health and Care Excellence.

However, the guidance on adults has recommended that some CAM practices (such as exclusion diets, dietary supplements and hyperbaric therapy) should not be used to treat the core features of autism (7).

The guidance on children and young people with autism recommended that some CAM practices (such as chelation and hyperbaric therapy) should not be used in any context. NICE also recommended that some CAM practices (such as neurofeedback training and auditory integration training) should not be used to address specific problems (such as speech and language difficulties) (8).

Supply, quality and regulation

The availability of CAM practices varies enormously from country to country. For example, in the UK, homeopathy is not available on the NHS in most areas of the country, with most homeopaths practicing privately. However, there are several NHS homeopathic hospitals and some GP practices also offer homeopathic treatment. Some homeopathic remedies are available from pharmacies.

The credentials required for complementary health practitioners vary tremendously from country to country and even within the same country, as well as from discipline to discipline. For example, there is no legal regulation of homeopathic practitioners in the UK. This means that anyone can practise as a homeopath, even if they have no qualifications or experience (9).

Costs and time

Costs: the price of undertaking a CAM practice depends on a number of factors including the specific practice, the practitioner, and the country in which it takes place. For example, in the UK the price for an initial consultation with a homeopath can vary from around £20 to £80. Homeopathic tablets or other products usually cost around £4 to £10 (9).

Time: the time required to undertake a CAM practice depends on a number of factors including the specific CAM practice, how the practitioner implements it and the characteristics of the individual patient.

Risks and safety

According to National Center for Complementary and Alternative Medicine:

'As with any medical product or treatment, there can be risks with complementary therapies. These risks depend on the specific therapy. Each therapy needs to be considered on its own.' (2)

Specific forms of complementary and alternative medicine

Whole medical systems

Introduction

Whole medical systems are complete systems of theory and practice that have evolved over time in different cultures and are separate from conventional or Western medicine.

There are many different systems including Ayurvedic medicine, homeopathy, naturopathy, and traditional Chinese medicine.

Each of these systems is used to treat a wide range of people with a wide range of conditions. For example, homeopathy is used to treat numerous conditions including asthma, depression and arthritis (9).

Whole medical systems are based on the idea of healing the whole person in a holistic manner, rather than just dealing with the immediate symptoms. So, for example Ayurvedic medicine stresses the importance of universal interconnectedness (among people, their health, and the universe), the body's constitution (prakriti), and life forces (dosha).

> ## Whole medical systems
>
> **Definition:** complete systems of medical theory and practice (for example homeopathy, naturopathy and traditional Chinese medicine).
>
> **Aims:** to heal the whole person in a holistic manner.
>
> **Who:** people with autism, including children and adults.
>
> **Evidence:** assessing possible benefits is difficult, due to the wide range of practices.
>
> **Risks:** vary between practices.

Ayurvedic physicians prescribe individualised treatments, including compounds of herbs or proprietary ingredients, and diet, exercise, and lifestyle recommendations (10).

Aims

Various claims have been made for whole medical systems in the treatment of people on the autism spectrum. For example, the following claims were made for massage based on traditional Chinese medicine:

'CCM massage treatments are typically tailored to each child's needs. Intensive, sustained special CCM massage programmes, combined with moderate moxibustion [the burning of the herb mugwort] ... , appropriate herbal prescriptions and special musical therapy can help the autistic children acquire better self-care, socialisation, and job skills.' (11)

Evidence

Determining the benefits of whole medical systems for individuals on the autism spectrum is difficult because they include such a wide range of practices. However, determining the benefits of most practices used within whole medical systems for individuals on the autism spectrum is not currently possible. We must wait for further research of sufficiently high quality to be completed (12).

According to the NHS Direct website, some whole medical systems (such as homeopathy) are scientifically implausible:

'There have been several reviews of the scientific evidence on the effectiveness of homeopathy. The House of Commons Science and Technology Committee said there is no evidence that homeopathy is effective as a treatment for any health condition.

'The ideas that underpin homeopathy are not accepted by mainstream science, and are not consistent with long-accepted principles on the way that the physical world works. The Committee's 2010 report on homeopathy said the "like cures like" principle is "theoretically weak", and that this is the "settled view of medical science"'. (9)

Risks and safety

Different whole medical systems appear to carry different risks. For example, according to the NHS website:

'Homeopathic remedies are generally safe and the risk of a serious adverse side effect arising from taking these remedies is thought to be small.' (9)

On the other hand, according to the National Center for Complementary and Alternative Medicine:

'Some Chinese herbal products may be safe, but others may not be. There have been reports of products being contaminated with drugs, toxins or heavy metals, or not containing the listed ingredients. Some of the herbs used in Chinese medicine can interact with drugs, can have serious side effects, or may be unsafe for people with certain medical conditions.' (13)

Natural products

Introduction

Natural products include a variety of herbal medicines (also known as botanicals), vitamins, minerals, and other 'natural products' such as essential fatty acids.

Many of these natural products are sold over the counter as dietary or nutritional supplements.

The idea behind the use of most natural products is to overcome nutritional or metabolic imbalances found in people on the autism spectrum, which are supposed to cause some of the symptoms of autism (such as impaired communication and social difficulties) and related issues (such as challenging behaviours) (14).

Natural products

Definition: a variety of herbal medicines, vitamins, minerals and other substances.

Aims: to overcome nutritional or metabolic imbalances.

Who: people with autism, including children and adults.

Evidence: assessing possible benefits is difficult, due to the wide range of practices.

Risks: vary between practices.

Aims

Various claims have been made for natural products as a treatment for people on the autism spectrum. For example, the following claims were reported in a systematic review of omega-3 fatty acids.

'Another study described parents' reports of improvement in general health, cognitive function, motor skills, sleeping, concentration, eye contact and sociability, and a reduction in aggression, irritability, and hyperactivity.' (15)

Evidence

Determining the benefits of natural products for individuals on the autism spectrum is difficult because there are so many different products. However, determining the benefits of most natural products for individuals on the autism spectrum is not currently possible. We must wait for further research of sufficiently high quality to be completed (16).

Risks and safety

Many natural products are safe provided you follow recommended daily doses published by reputable organisations, such as the Food Standards Agency.

Some dietary supplements contain active ingredients that can have strong effects in the body. For example, too much vitamin A can cause headaches and liver damage, reduce bone strength, and cause birth defects (17).

Additional information

Please see Chapter 19 for our detailed entries on dietary supplements on page 205.

Mind-body medicine

Introduction

Mind and body practices focus on the interactions between the brain, mind, body, and behaviour.

Mind-body practices include:

- meditation-based activities such as deep-breathing exercises, guided imagery, hypnotherapy and progressive relaxation
- TCM/martial arts-based activities such as acupuncture, qi gong, tai chi and yoga
- other practices including the Feldenkrais method, the Alexander technique, pilates, Rolfing Structural Integration, and Trager psychophysical integration.

The idea behind mind-body practices is that the mind and the body can be used to affect physical functioning and to promote health (1).

> ### Mind-body medicine
>
> **Definition:** a range of practices which focus on the interactions between the brain, mind, body, and behaviour.
>
> **Aims:** to promote health and affect physical function.
>
> **Who:** people with autism, including children and adults.
>
> **Evidence:** assessing possible benefits is difficult, due to the wide range of practices.
>
> **Risks:** vary between practices.

Aims

Various claims have been made for mind-body practices. For example, one review of acupuncture reported a study which claimed:

'The results showed statistically significant improvements in comprehension, cognition and parental reports regarding social initiation, receptive language, motor skills and attention span in those who received [acupuncture].' (18)

Evidence

Determining the benefits of mind-body medicine for individuals on the autism spectrum is difficult because it includes such a wide range of practices. However, determining the benefits of specific mind-body medicine practices for individuals on the autism spectrum is not currently possible. We must wait for further research of sufficiently high quality to be completed (19).

Risks and safety

Many mind-body practices, such as tai chi, appear to be relatively safe as they rely on slow, careful movements. However some mind-body practices, such as acupuncture, may pose some risks to a small number of people:

'Relatively few complications from the use of acupuncture have been reported to the FDA, in light of the millions of people treated each year and the number of acupuncture needles used. Still, complications have resulted from inadequate sterilization of needles and from improper delivery of treatments. ... When not delivered properly, acupuncture can cause serious adverse effects, including infections and punctured organs.' (20)

Manipulative and body-based practices

Introduction

Manipulative and body-based practices focus primarily on the structures and systems of the body, including the bones and joints, soft tissues, and circulatory and lymphatic systems.

Manipulative and body-based practices include chiropractic, cranial osteopathy and massage.

The idea behind the use of manipulative and body-based practices is that the structures and systems of the body can be changed to affect physical functioning and to promote health (1).

Manipulative and body-based practices

Definition: a range of practices which focus primarily on the structures and systems of the body, such as the bones and joints.

Aims: to promote health and affect physical functioning.

Who: people with autism, including children and adults.

Evidence: assessing possible benefits is difficult, due to the wide range of practices.

Risks: vary between practices.

Aims

Various claims have been made for the use of manipulative and body-based practices as a treatment for people on the autism spectrum. For example, one review of chiropractic reported on a study which stated:

'The most common improvements observed [in children with autism] were in communication, verbal skills, the ability to make eye contact, improved mood, and physical sport skills.' (21)

Evidence

Determining the benefits of manipulative and body-based practices for individuals on the autism spectrum is difficult because there are so many different practices. However, determining the benefits of most manipulative and body-based practices for individuals on the autism spectrum is not currently possible. We must wait for further research of sufficiently high quality to be completed (22).

Risks and safety

Some manipulative and body-based practices may carry some risks. For example, the National Center for Complementary and Alternative Medicine (2012) reported that:

'Side effects from spinal manipulation can include temporary headaches, tiredness, or discomfort in the parts of the body that were treated.' (23)

Energy medicine

Introduction

Energy medicine involves the manipulation of various energy fields, which may or may not be measurable by scientists.

Veritable energy therapies include practices based on objectively measurable forms of energy such as electromagnetic fields, for example, neurofeedback training, transcranial direct-current stimulation and transcranial magnetic stimulation.

Energy medicine

Definition: practices based on the manipulation of energy fields.

Aims: to manipulate energy fields in order to improve various features of autism.

Who: people with autism, including children and adults.

Evidence: assessing possible benefits is difficult, due to the wide range of practices.

Risks: vary between practices.

Putative energy therapies describe practices based on yet-to-be-measured energy fields (also called biofields). These therapies generally reflect the concept that human beings are infused with subtle forms of energy, including spiritual energy. Putative energy practices include qigong, reiki and tai chi (1).

Aims

There have been various claims made for energy medicine. For example, Silva *et al* (2011) reported:

'Treatment of young children with autism with kai qiao tuina/ qigong sensory training resulted in a decrease in sensory and self-regulatory impairment and a reduction in severity of measures of autism.' (24)

Evidence

Determining the benefits of energy medicine for individuals on the autism spectrum is difficult because it includes such a wide range of practices. However, determining the benefits of most practices within energy medicine for individuals on the autism spectrum is not currently possible. We must wait for further research of sufficiently high quality to be completed (25).

Risks and safety

No significant risks appear to be associated with putative energy practices, such as qigong.

Some risks are associated with some veritable energy practices, such as transcranial magnetic stimulation. For example, there have been reports of seizures, painful scalp sensations, facial twitching and hearing problems due to the loud clicking noise emitted by the TMS machine (26, 27).

Other CAM interventions

Some CAM interventions do not readily fit into any of the categories above, including animal-assisted activities and therapies such as assistance dogs, dolphin therapy, hippotherapy and pet therapy.

Please see Chapter 25 for our detailed entry on animal-assisted activities and therapies on page 267.

Further information

In this book: Please see How to use this book (page 11), Chapter 3 (page 38) for information about interventions, Chapter 4 (page 43) for information about how scientists evaluate those interventions, and section 3 (page 284) for advice on making the decision about whether or not to use a specific intervention.

Website: Please see www.researchautism.net/complementary-and-alternative-medicine for information about complementary and alternative medicine including information about specific interventions and details of scientific studies and trials.

References

1. National Center for Complementary and Alternative Medicine (2008) *What is Complementary and Alternative Medicine?* Bethesda, MD: National Center for Complementary and Alternative Medicine.

2. National Center for Complementary and Alternative Medicine (2013) *Are You Considering Complementary Medicine?* Bethesda, MD: National Center for Complementary and Alternative Medicine.

3. Brown KA & Patel DR (2005) Complementary and alternative medicine in developmental disabilities. *Indian Journal of Pediatrics* **72** 949–52.

4. Levy S & Hyman S (2008) Complementary and alternative medicine treatments for children with autism spectrum disorders. *Child and Adolescent Psychiatric Clinics of North America* **17** 803–820.

5. Levy SE & Hyman SL (2005) Novel treatments for autistic spectrum disorders. *Mental Retardation and Developmental Disabilities* **11** 131–142.

6. Schechtman MA (2007) Scientifically unsupported therapies in the treatment of young children with autism spectrum disorders. *Pediatric Annals* **36** 497–498; 500–502; 504–505.

7. National Institute for Health and Care Excellence (2012) *Autism: Recognition, referral, diagnosis and management of adults on the autism spectrum*. London: National Institute for Health and Care Excellence.

8. National Institute for Health and Care Excellence (2013) *The Management and Support of Children and Young People on the Autism Spectrum*. London: National Institute for Health and Care Excellence.

9. NHS Choices (2013) *Homeopathy*. London, UK: NHS.

10. National Center for Complementary and Alternative Medicine (2013) *Ayurvedic Medicine: An introduction*. Bethesda, MD: National Center for Complementary and Alternative Medicine.

11. Zhang J (2010) A review of autism spectrum disorders (ASD) from a perspective of classical Chinese medicine (CCM). *Journal of Traditional Chinese Medicine* **30** 53–59.

12. Research Autism (2014) *Whole medical systems and autism* [online]. Available at: http://www.researchautism.net/whole-medical-systems (accessed January 13, 2015).

13. National Center for Complementary and Alternative Medicine (2009) *Traditional Chinese Medicine: An introduction*. Bethesda, MD: National Center for Complementary and Alternative Medicine.

14. Adams JB (2007) *Summary of Biomedical Treatments for Autism*. San Diego, CA: Autism Research Institute.

15. James S, Montgomery P & Williams KJ (2009) Omega-3 fatty acids supplementation for autism spectrum disorders (ASD). *Cochrane Database of Systematic Reviews* **9**.

16. Research Autism (2014) *Natural products and autism* [online]. Available at: http://www.researchautism.net/natural-products (accessed January 13, 2015).

17. Office of Dietary Supplements (2006) *Dietary Supplement Fact Sheet: Vitamin A and carotenoids*. Bethesda, MD: Office of Dietary Supplements.

18. Lee MS, Choi T-Y, Shin B-C & Ernst E (2012) Acupuncture for children with autism spectrum disorders: a systematic review of randomized clinical trials. *Journal of Autism and Developmental Disorders* **42** 1671–83.

19. Research Autism (2014) *Mind body medicine and autism* [online]. Available at: http://www.researchautism.net/mind-body-medicine (accessed January 13, 2015).

20. National Center for Complementary and Alternative Medicine (2011) *Acupuncture*. Bethesda, MD: National Center for Complementary and Alternative Medicine.

21. Alcantara J, Alcantara JD & Alcantara J (2011) A systematic review of the literature on the chiropractic care of patients with autism spectrum disorder. *Explore (New York, NY)* **7** 384–90.

22. Research Autism (2014) *Manipulative and body-based practices and autism* [online]. Available at: www.researchautism.net/manipulative-and-body-based-practices (accessed January 13, 2015).

23. National Center for Complementary and Alternative Medicine (2012) *Chiropractic: An introduction*. Bethesda, MD: National Center for Complementary and Alternative Medicine.

24. Silva LMT, Schalock M & Ayres R (2011) A model and treatment for autism at the convergence of Chinese medicine and Western science: first 130 cases. *Chinese Journal of Integrative Medicine* **17** 421–9.

25. Research Autism (2014) *Energy medicine and autism* [online]. Available at: www.researchautism.net/energy-medicine (accessed January 13, 2015).

26. Wassermann EM (1998) Risk and safety of repetitive transcranial magnetic stimulation: report and suggested guidelines from the International Workshop on the Safety of Repetitive Transcranial Magnetic Stimulation, June 5–7, 1996. *Electroencephalography and Clinical Neurophysiology* **108** 1–16.

27. Oberman LM, Rotenberg A & Pascual-Leone A (2015) Use of transcranial magnetic stimulation in autism spectrum disorders. *Journal of Autism and Developmental Disorders* **45** 524–536.

Chapter 7:
Alternative and augmentative communication

Introduction

Alternative and augmentative communication (AAC) is any form of communication that people use if they are unable or unwilling to use standard forms of communication such as speech.

Alternative communication systems are designed to replace standard means of communication. Augmentative communication systems are designed to complement and sometimes enhance standard means of communication.

Unaided AAC include those forms of communication (such as sign language) which do not require external tools, devices or equipment.

Aided AAC includes those forms of communication (such as voice output communication aids) which do require external tools, devices or equipment.

Some people think that some forms of AAC may be especially appropriate for those people on the autism spectrum who find it difficult to use standard forms of communication.

Evidence

Very strong research evidence shows that many people on the autism spectrum struggle to communicate using traditional communication methods. For example, they may be non-verbal or find it difficult to hold a conversation with another person (1).

Determining the benefits of some forms of alternative and augmentative communication (such as sign language and voice output communication aids) is not currently possible. We must wait for further research of sufficiently high quality to be completed (2, 3).

There is evidence that the Picture Exchange Communication System may help some children and adolescents on the autism spectrum to communicate more effectively according to some very limited research evidence of sufficiently high quality (4).

There is evidence that facilitated communication is not effective in supporting people on the autism spectrum to communicate more effectively according to some extremely limited research evidence of sufficiently high quality (5).

NICE guidelines

The National Institute for Health and Care Excellence reported:

'Many people with autism experience significant communication problems (for example, the absence of any spoken language or significant deficits in interpersonal skills), which have a profound effect on their ability to lead a full and rewarding life. It is probable that these problems are related to the core symptoms of autism and are likely to persist for most people given the life-long course of autism and the lack of effective interventions for these core symptoms. A number of communication devices have been developed for autism but few, if any, have been subjected to a proper evaluation in adults.' (6)

It also recommended:

'Do not provide facilitated communication for adults with autism.' (6)

Supply, quality and regulation

In theory, most people can learn how to provide unaided forms of AAC, such as sign language, by attending training courses or teaching themselves. However we would recommend that you consult your care team first, especially the speech and language therapist, if you are thinking of using any unaided forms of AAC, such as sign language.

Most people can obtain aided forms of AAC, such as voice output communication aids, by purchasing them from the suppliers. Again, we would recommend that you consult your care team first, especially the speech and language therapist, if you are thinking of using an alternative and augmentative communication device.

The different forms of AAC may be provided by a variety of professionals including speech and language therapists, teachers and others. Each of these will have their own regulating body. For example, speech and language therapists must be registered with the Health and Care Professions Council, and may also be chartered with the Royal College of Speech and Language Therapy.

Costs and time

Costs: the cost of the different forms of AAC depends mostly on the specific form of AAC being used. Costs may include the purchase of equipment (such as a voice output communication aid) and the costs of attending training courses/purchasing training materials (for interventions such as sign language).

The cost will also vary depending on who is working with the recipient of the intervention. For example, if the person is a paid employee, the cost can be high. If a parent or carer is working with the child, the cost might be quite low.

Time: the amount of time required to use the different forms of AAC will depend to a large extent on the specific form of AAC being used. However, in most cases, the time required may be significant. For example, it may take time to learn how to use sign language, to teach it to the person on the autism spectrum, and then to use it every day.

Risks and safety

No risks are known for most forms of AAC. However, some significant risks exist for facilitated communication, including the danger of unsubstantiated claims of sexual abuse against family members of the person with autism (6).

Specific forms of alternative and augmentative communication

Facilitated communication

Introduction

Facilitated communication (also known as supported typing) is a form of alternative and augmentative communication in which someone physically supports a disabled person and helps them to point at pictures or words.

Facilitated communication is based on the idea that many of the difficulties faced by disabled people are due to movement difficulties rather than social or communication difficulties.

> **Facilitated communication**
>
> **Definition:** a facilitator physically supports a disabled person and helps them to point at pictures or words.
>
> **Aims:** improve social communication, make choices.
>
> **Who:** people with autism who are non-verbal.
>
> **Evidence:** extremely limited, low-quality research suggests it does not help people with autism.
>
> **Risks:** significant harm.

The communication partner (usually called a facilitator) physically supports the disabled person so that they can point to pictures, symbols, letters and words using a computer keyboard, letter books or picture books. By doing this, the disabled person can demonstrate what they want to communicate.

Some disabled people who use facilitated communication often use it as part of a total communication approach. For example, they may use it in combination with other methods of communication such as speech or sign language (7).

Aims

Some people think that facilitated communication may be appropriate for people on the autism spectrum who are unable to speak and who are also unable to write or type for themselves.

They think that these people are unable to write or type for themselves because of movement difficulties rather than because of any social or communication difficulties.

They think that the facilitator will help the person to overcome the physical difficulties, enabling them to point to the pictures or letters that they want to use.

These people think that some people on the autism spectrum can eventually learn how to type for themselves, enabling them to communicate independently (7).

Evidence

There is evidence that facilitated communication is not effective in supporting people on the autism spectrum to communicate more effectively according to some extremely limited research evidence of sufficiently high quality.

The research suggests that, consciously or unconsciously, the facilitators are controlling what is written by the person they are assisting. Generally, no indication of spontaneous communication by clients is shown (5).

Risks and safety

A risk to individuals on the autism spectrum is that facilitated communication may make the participant more passive and less likely to initiate communication.

Members of the family are also at risk. For example, according to NICE:

'... there is evidence that facilitated communication can lead to significant harm; for instance, unsubstantiated claims of sexual abuse against family members have been made while using facilitated communication.' (6)

Additional information

The American Academy of Pediatrics Council on Children With Disabilities, the American Academy of Child and Adolescent Psychiatry and the American Association on Mental Retardation are all highly critical of facilitated communication and strongly recommend that it is not used (8, 9, 10).

Picture Exchange Communication System

Introduction

In the Picture Exchange Communication System, (PECS) a child is taught to communicate with an adult by giving them a card with a picture on it.

PECS is based on the idea that children who can't talk or write can be taught to communicate using pictures.

The adult begins by teaching the child to exchange a picture of an item they want. For example, if the child wants a drink, he will give a picture of a drink to the adult who will then give them a drink.

> ## PECS
>
> **Definition:** a child is taught to communicate with an adult by giving her a card with a picture on it.
>
> **Aims:** to improve social communication, make choices.
>
> **Who:** people with autism who are non-verbal.
>
> **Evidence:** very limited amount of research evidence that PECS may provide some benefits.
>
> **Risks:** none.

The adult will then teach the child progressively more difficult skills, such as using pictures to make whole sentences or to express preferences (11, 12).

Aims

Some people think that PECS can be used to help non-verbal children and adults on the autism spectrum to initiate communication and to express their needs.

They think it can also be used to teach some non-verbal children with autism to speak.

Some people think it can also be used with people who have a wide range of other communicative, cognitive and physical difficulties (12).

Evidence

PECS may provide some benefits for some individuals on the autism spectrum according to a very limited amount of research evidence of sufficiently high quality (4).

Risks and safety

No risks are known with the use of PECS for individuals on the autism spectrum.

Additional information

The Picture Exchange Communication System is a key element in many multi-component programmes and approaches – such as the SPELL approach and the TEACCH programme.

Sign language

Introduction

Sign languages use hand shape, position, and movement; body movements; gestures; facial expressions; and other visual cues to form words.

Sign languages include American Sign Language, British Sign Language and Makaton.

Most of these languages are completely separate from spoken English. Each contains all the fundamental features a language needs to function on its own. For example, each has its own rules for grammar, punctuation, and word order.

Sign language

Definition: languages which use various movements and expressions to form words.

Aims: improve social communication.

Who: people with speech or language difficulties.

Evidence: assessing the possible benefits is difficult due to the wide range of practices. Insufficient research to determine if sign language has any benefits.

Risks: none.

Some sign languages (such as Sign Supported English) take the signs from another language (such as British Sign Language) and use them in the order that the words would be spoken in the spoken language (English) (11).

Aims

Sign languages are used by a variety of people with speech and language difficulties including some people with autism.

Some people think that sign language is a useful tool for some people on the autism spectrum because it does not require them to use spoken language.

They think that teaching those on the spectrum to use sign language can help them to communicate and, in some cases, may help them to learn to speak (11).

Evidence

Determining the benefits of sign language for individuals on the autism spectrum is not currently possible. We must wait for further research of sufficiently high quality to be completed (2).

Risks and safety

No risks are known with the use of sign language for individuals on the autism spectrum.

Additional information

Sign language is sometimes used, alone or alongside the spoken word, to teach individuals with disabilities to communicate.

Voice output communication aids

Introduction

Voice output communication aids (VOCAs) or speech-generating devices (SGDs) are devices which speak for the user.

The simplest VOCAs store a single pre-recorded message, which is produced as digitised speech when the person using the device presses a button, switch, or key.

The most elaborate VOCAs include software that allows users to create and combine words to produce novel sentences in computerised speech.

Many mobile devices, such as phones and tablets, now provide similar functions to the traditional VOCAs (13, 14).

VOCAs

Definition: speech-generating devices.

Aims: to improve social communication.

Who: non-verbal individuals with disabilities.

Evidence: insufficient research to determine if particular VOCAs have any benefits.

Risks: none.

Aims

Voice output communication aids are designed for a variety of people with disabilities who find it difficult to speak, including some people on the autism spectrum.

Some people think that voice output communication aids are a useful tool for some people on the autism spectrum because it enables them to communicate via the device rather than having to speak for themselves.

Some people think that VOCAs may also encourage some non-verbal individuals on the autism spectrum to learn to speak for themselves (13, 14).

Evidence

Determining the benefits of voice output communication aids for individuals on the autism spectrum is not currently possible. We must wait for further research of sufficiently high quality to be completed (3).

> ## Further information
>
> **In this book:** Please see How to use this book (page 11), Chapter 3 (page 38) for information about interventions, Chapter 4 (page 43) for information about how scientists evaluate those interventions, and Section 3 (page 284) for advice on making the decision about whether or not to use a specific intervention.
>
> **Website:** Please see www.researchautism.net/alternative-and-augmentative-communication for information about alternative and augmentative communication, including information about specific forms of communication and details of scientific studies and trials.

References

1. National Institute for Health and Care Excellence (2013) *The Management and Support of Children and Young People on the Autism Spectrum*. London: National Institute for Health and Care Excellence.

2. Research Autism (2014) *Sign language and autism* [online]. Available at: www.researchautism.net/sign-language-and-autism (accessed January 13, 2015).

3. Research Autism (2014) *Voice output communication aids and autism*. [online]. Available at: www.researchautism.net/vocas-and-autism (accessed January 13, 2015).

4. Research Autism (2014) *PECS and autism* [online]. Available at: www.researchautism.net/pecs-and-autism (accessed January 13, 2015).

5. Research Autism (2014) *Facilitated communication and autism* [online]. Available at: www.researchautism.net/facilitated-communication-and-autism (accessed January 13, 2015).

6. National Institute for Health and Care Excellence (2012) *Autism: Recognition, referral, diagnosis and management of adults on the autism spectrum*. London: National Institute for Health and Care Excellence.

7. Mostert MP (2012) Facilitated communication: the empirical imperative to prevent further professional malpractice. *Evidence-Based Communication Assessment and Intervention* **6** 18–27.

8. American Academy of Pediatrics Council on Children With Disabilities (1998) Auditory integration training and facilitated communication for autism *Pediatrics*. **102**(2) 431–433.

9. American Academy of Child and Adolescent Psychiatry *Policy statement of facilitated communication*. AACAP Newsletter, February 1994.

10. American Association on Mental Retardation (1994). AAMR Board approves policy on facilitated communication. *AAMR News & Notes* **7** (1) 1.

11. Mirenda P (2003) Toward functional augmentative and alternative communication for students with autism: Manual signs, graphic symbols, and voice output communication aids. *Language, Speech, and Hearing Services in Schools* **34** 203–216.

12. Ganz JB, Davis JL, Lund EM, Goodwyn FD & Simpson RL (2012) Meta-analysis of PECS with individuals with ASD: investigation of targeted versus non-targeted outcomes, participant characteristics, and implementation phase. *Research in Developmental Disabilities* **33** 406–18.

13. Van der Meer LA & Rispoli M (2010) Communication interventions involving speech-generating devices for children with autism: a review of the literature. *Developmental Neurorehabilitation* **13** 294–306.

14. Lancioni GE et al (2006) PECS and VOCAs to enable students with developmental disabilities to make requests: an overview of the literature. *Research in Developmental Disabilities* **28** 468–88.

Chapter 8:
Assistive and adaptive technology

Introduction

Assistive and adaptive technology refers to products, devices or equipment that are used to maintain, increase or improve the capabilities of individuals with disabilities (1).

Assistive and adaptive technology is based on the idea that different types of technology can be used to help people overcome practical difficulties, such as problems with communication or self-regulation.

A wide range of different interventions exist, using a wide range of different devices and equipment, which may be divided into high tech (uses electronic equipment) and low tech (does not use electronic equipment).

Here we focus on some interventions which use high-technology systems, such as apps, biofeedback and transcranial stimulation. For details of interventions based on low tech systems, please see Chapter 16 on Technology-based behavioural interventions on page 161.

Evidence

Determining the benefits of most forms of assistive and adaptive technology for people with autism is not currently possible. We must wait for further research of sufficiently high quality to be completed.

This may be because some technologies, such as apps, are too new to have a solid evidence base. However this situation may change in the next few years as there are several research projects underway at present (2, 3, 4).

NICE guidelines

The National Institute for Health and Care Excellence did not make any recommendations on most forms of assistive and adaptive technology but it did recommend (5):

'Do not use neurofeedback to manage speech and language problems in children and young people with autism.'

Supply, quality and regulation

You can obtain some forms of assistive and adaptive technology, such as mobile devices, apps or computers, by purchasing them direct from the suppliers. However we would recommend that you consult your care team first, especially the speech and language therapist, if you are thinking of using an alternative and augmentative communication device. In other cases, you are always likely to need help from a professional. For example, transcranial magnetic stimulation is normally delivered by a trained professional in a medical or research facility.

Some regulating authorities oversee some specific forms of assistive and adaptive technology in some countries. For example, the US Food and Drug Administration has issued guidance on the use of transcranial magnetic stimulation devices. However, no regulatory system exists for most forms of technology, such as apps or neurofeedback training, in most countries (6).

Costs and time

Costs: the cost of different forms of assistive and adaptive technology will depend to a large extent on the specific form of assistive and adaptive technology being used. Costs may include the purchase of equipment and the cost of attending training courses and purchasing training materials. The cost will also vary depending on who is working with the recipient of the intervention. For example, if the person is a paid employee, the cost can be high. If a parent or carer is working with the child, the cost can be quite low.

Time: the amount of time required to use different forms of assistive and adaptive technology will depend to a large extent on the specific form of technology being used as well as on the needs of the individual. For example, transcranial magnetic stimulation is normally delivered in several sessions at a medical or academic facility. Additional time may be required for travel to the facility.

Risks and safety

Different forms of assistive and adaptive technology pose different risks. For example, no risks are known for biofeedback but transcranial magnetic stimulation can sometimes produce seizures, painful scalp sensations, facial twitching and hearing problems (7).

Specific forms of assistive and adaptive technology

Apps

Introduction

An app is a computer application. Most people use the term app to refer to a computer programme (software) that can be downloaded and used on an electronic device, such as a mobile phone or a tablet.

An enormous range of apps is available and they all do different things (for example there are apps that forecast the weather, apps for well-known news providers, and games).

Apps

Definition: an app is a computer application. Apps can provide easily accessible interventions for people with autism.

Aims: unique to each app.

Who: people with autism of all ages and all levels of ability (although not all apps will be appropriate for everyone).

Evidence: insufficient evidence to determine if particular apps have any benefits.

Risks: unique to each app.

Aims

There are a number of apps which have been specifically designed to help people on the autism spectrum and each one will be designed to achieve different aims.

For example, the ReacTickles apps use touch, gesture and audio input to encourage interactive communication. Other apps provide help with life skills and literacy, provide social stories and visual schedules, or are games specifically designed for people with autism.

Some apps can be used by people with autism of any age and any ability while other apps may be more appropriate for people who can deal with complex systems and processes (8, 9).

Evidence

A large number of apps are aimed at people with autism, and new apps appear on a regular basis. So it is extremely difficult to study every app. Some apps are based on established interventions, such as the Picture Exchange Communication System (PECS), but the apps themselves have not been tested for effectiveness. Determining the benefits of any specific app for people on the autism spectrum is not currently possible. We must wait for further research of sufficiently high quality to be completed (2).

Risks and safety

No risks are known for most apps.

Additional information

The growing use of apps for people with autism is partly because of evidence that people with autism enjoy using computers and electronic devices such as mobile phones and tablets, so they may be more motivated to access an intervention provided on one of these. Furthermore, as tablets, mobile phones and computers are so widely used, a person with autism using an intervention on one of these devices will not stand out and this can help them blend in and be more accepted by society (10).

Auditory integration training

Auditory integration training is designed to improve a person's ability to process sounds by 're-educating' the brain. This is done by playing electronically modified music in which the frequencies have been changed.

For more information, please see Chapter 21 on motor-sensory interventions on page 229.

Biofeedback

Introduction

Biofeedback includes a range of therapies in which you are taught to control your own physiological functions such as brain waves, heart rate or muscle tension. During a biofeedback session, electrodes are attached to your skin. These electrodes/sensors send signals to a monitor, which displays a sound, flash of light, or image that represents heart and breathing rate etc. A biofeedback therapist helps you practice relaxation exercises, which you fine-tune to control different body functions. Over time you learn to use that feedback to change those functions. So, for example, you may learn to slow down your heart rate by seeing it displayed on a monitor.

> ### Biofeedback
>
> **Definition:** a range of therapies which teach a person to regulate their own physiological functions, such as brain waves, muscle tension, or heart rate.
>
> **Aims:** varies.
>
> **Who:** people with autism of any age and ability who can understand the training.
>
> **Evidence:** insufficient evidence to determine if biofeedback has any benefits.
>
> **Risks:** none.

- **EEG biofeedback (Neurofeedback):** Monitors and controls brain waves. Used to improve attention, impulsivity, hyperactivity, and IQ.

- **EMG biofeedback (Electromyogram):** Monitors and controls muscle activity and tension. Used for back pain, headaches, anxiety disorders, muscle retraining after injury, and incontinence.
- **HRA biofeedback (Heart rate variability):** Monitors and controls heart rate. Used for anxiety, asthma, chronic obstructive pulmonary disease and irregular heartbeat (11).

Aims

Biofeedback is designed to be used on people of any age and any ability, as long as they are able to understand the aim of the training.

Some people think that EEG biofeedback can be used to help people on the autism spectrum to control their brainwaves, which will help them to deal with a wide range of issues including the core symptoms of autism, attention, executive function, language and visual perception (12, 13).

Some people think that HRA biofeedback can be used to help people on the autism spectrum to control their breathing and heart rate and regulate physiological arousal, and in turn reduce reported symptoms of anxiety, depression, attention, and behavioural difficulties (14).

Evidence

Determining the benefits of biofeedback for people with autism is not currently possible. We must wait for further research of sufficiently high quality to be completed (3).

Risks and safety

No risks are known for biofeedback.

Hyperbaric therapy

Hyperbaric therapy is the medical use of oxygen at higher-than-atmospheric pressure. The oxygen is administered to the individual in a pressurised chamber, with the goal of increasing oxygen absorption in bodily tissue.

For more information, please see Chapter 20 on Alternative medical procedures on page 219.

Mobile (portable) devices

Mobile or portable devices include any electronic devices that can be easily carried by one person. Mobile devices include cell phones (such as iPhones), MP3 players (such as iPlayers), laptops, personal digital assistants (such as Palms), prompting devices (such as pagers), tablets (such as iPads), etc. as well as some voice output communication aids (also known as speech generating devices).

Please see the entry on Apps in this chapter for more information about mobile devices such as phones and MP3 players. Please see the entry on 'Voice output communication aids' in Chapter 7 on Alternative and augmentative communication on page 90 for more information about them.

Transcranial stimulation

Introduction

Transcranial stimulation describes a number of different treatments which use painless electro-magnetic fields to stimulate nerve cells in the brain.

- **Transcranial direct stimulation (tDCS):** A constant, low intensity current is passed through two electrodes placed over the head. Anodal stimulation is designed to excite brain cell activity while cathodal

Transcranial stimulation

Definition: procedures that use electro-magnetic fields to stimulate nerve cells in the brain.

Aims: to target the core features of autism.

Who: adults with autism.

Evidence: insufficient evidence to determine if rTMS or tCDS have any benefits.

Risks: some risks are associated with both rTDCS and rTMS.

stimulation is designed to inhibit or reduce brain cell activity. tDCS is commonly used to treat a range of conditions such as depression, anxiety, Parkinson's disease, and chronic pain (15).

- **Transcranial magnetic stimulation (TMS):** An electromagnetic coil is held against the forehead near an area of the brain that is thought to be involved in mood regulation. Then, short electromagnetic pulses are administered through the coil. rTMS is a specific form of TMS in which the pulses are repeated. TMS is used to treat a range of conditions including depression, Alzheimer's disease and epilepsy (16).

Aims

tDCS and rTMS are designed to be used on adults of any ability provided they do not fall into one of several groups for whom it may be contraindicated eg. people with epilepsy. Due to the lack of data on the side effects of TMS in children, it has been suggested that TMS should only be used if there is a clear clinical reason, such as refractory epilepsy. Therefore, TMS should not be used in children with autism (16).

Some people think that tDCS can be used to help people on the autism spectrum in a number of areas including social interaction, hyperactivity and irritability (15).

Some people think that rTMS can be used to decrease repetitive behaviours and irritability and to improve attention in some people on the autism spectrum (16).

Evidence

Determining the benefits of any form of transcranial stimulation for people with autism is not currently possible. We must wait for further research of sufficiently high quality to be completed (4).

Risks and safety

The most common side effects of tDCS are mild tingling sensations, light itching sensation, moderate fatigue and headache (17). Some risks are associated with rTMS. Seizures, painful scalp sensations, facial twitching and hearing problems due to the loud clicking noise emitted by the TMS machine have all been reported (7).

Additional information

rTMS requires patients to be completely immobilised in a prefixed position for tens of minutes at a time.

Video modelling

Video modelling is a method of teaching in which an individual learns a behaviour or a skill by watching a video recording of someone – the model – demonstrating that behaviour or skill. The model can be someone else – such as a parent or sibling – or it can be the individual him/herself – when the process is called video self-modelling (VSM). For more information, please see Chapter 16 on Technology-based behavioural interventions on page 161.

Further information

In this book: Please see How to use this book (page 11), Chapter 3 (page 38) for information about interventions, Chapter 4 (page 43) for information about how scientists evaluate those interventions, and Section 3 (page 284) for advice on making the decision about whether or not to use a specific intervention.

Websites: Please see www.researchautism.net/assistive-and-adaptive-technology for information about assistive and adaptive technology including information about specific forms of technology and details of scientific studies and trials.

References

1. The Technology-Related Assistance for Individuals with Disabilities Act (1988).

2. Research Autism (2014) *Apps and autism* [online]. Available at: www.researchautism.net/apps (accessed January 13, 2015).

3. Research Autism (2014) *Biofeedback and autism* [online]. Available at: www.researchautism.net/biofeedback (accessed January 13, 2015).

4. Research Autism (2014) *Transcranial stimulation and autism* [online]. Available at: www.researchautism.net/transcranial-stimulation (accessed January 13, 2015).

5. National Institute for Health and Care Excellence (2013) *The Management and Support of Children and Young People on the Autism Spectrum*. London: National Institute for Health and Care Excellence.

6. Food and Drug Administration (2011) *Guidance for Industry and FDA Staff - Class II Special Controls Guidance Document: Repetitive Transcranial Magnetic Stimulation (rTMS) Systems*. Silver Spring, MD: Food and Drug Administration.

7. Rossi S, Hallett M, Rossini PM & Pascual-Leone A (2009) Safety, ethical considerations, and application guidelines for the use of transcranial magnetic stimulation in clinical practice and research. *Clinical Neurophysiology: Official Journal of the International Federation of Clinical Neurophysiology* **120** 2008–20039.

8. ReacTickles Magic (2011) About ReacTickles Magic. Available at: http://reactickles.org/about/ (accessed January 13, 2015).

9. Fletcher-Watson S (2013) A targeted review of computer-assisted learning for people with autism spectrum disorder: towards a consistent methodology. *Review Journal of Autism and Developmental Disorders* **1** 87–100.

10. Grynszpan O, Weiss PLT, Perez-Diaz F & Gal E (2014) Innovative technology-based interventions for autism spectrum disorders: a meta-analysis. *Autism: The International Journal of Research and Practice* **18** 346–61.

11. Kiefer D (2014) *Overview of Biofeedback*. New York, NY: Web MD.

12. Coben R, Linden M & Myers TE (2010) Neurofeedback for autistic spectrum disorder: a review of the literature. *Applied Psychophysiology and Biofeedback* **35** 83–105.

13. Holtmann M, Steiner S, Hohmann S, Poustka L, Banaschewski T & Bölte S (2011) Neurofeedback in autism spectrum disorders. *Developmental Medicine and Child Neurology* **53** 986–93.

14. Berger MJ (2007) The efficacy of selected biofeedback techniques in mitigating symptoms associated with autism spectrum disorder. *Biofeedback* **35** 62–68.

15. D'Urso G Ferrucci R, Bruzzese D, Pascotto A, Priori A, Altamura CA, Galderisi S & Bravaccio C. (2014) Transcranial direct current stimulation for autistic disorder. *Biological Psychiatry* **76** e5–e6.

16. Oberman LM, Rotenberg A & Pascual-Leone A (2013) Use of transcranial magnetic stimulation in autism spectrum disorders. *Journal of Autism and Developmental Disorders* **45** 524-536.

17. Brunoni AR, Nitsche MA, Bolognini N, Bikson M, Wagner T, Merabet L, Edwards DJ, Valero-Cabre A, Rotenberg A, Pascual-Leone A, Ferrucci R, Priori A, Boggio PS & Fregni F (2012) Clinical research with transcranial direct current stimulation (tDCS): challenges and future directions. *Brain Stimulation* **5** 175–195.

Chapter 9:
Behavioural and developmental interventions

Introduction

Behavioural and developmental interventions are a very wide group of interventions that include many other types of intervention. These other interventions include some that are described as educational, psychosocial, or psychological interventions.

Behavioural interventions are designed to encourage appropriate behaviour (such as getting dressed or talking to other people) and to discourage inappropriate behaviour (such as self-harm or aggression towards others). The people intervening, who could be therapists, teachers or parents, often break down the desired behaviours into small, achievable tasks which are then taught in a very structured manner.

Developmental interventions are designed to target core developmental areas within the individual rather than his or her outward behaviours. Therapists, teachers and parents work with the individual's own interests or actions to slowly build engagement, interaction, communication, affection, and then specific skills such as logical reasoning and symbolic thinking.

In practice, many interventions (such as the National Autistic Society's EarlyBird Programme) include both behavioural and developmental elements. Many specific techniques (such as modelling, that is, demonstrating desirable behaviour and reinforcing, such as praising desirable behaviour) are also used within both behavioural and developmental interventions. And many of these approaches and techniques are used within educational and vocational interventions.

We have categorised behavioural and developmental interventions as follows (although there are many other ways in which they can be categorised):

- behavioural
- developmental
- comprehensive, multi-component
- parent-training and support
- relationship-based
- specific functions
- technology-based.

We cover each category in its own chapter, so please turn to the chapter that interests you.

> ## Further information
>
> **In this book:** Please see How to use this book (page 11), Chapter 3 (page 38) for information about interventions, Chapter 4 (page 43) for information about how scientists evaluate those interventions, and Section 3 (page 284) for advice on making the decision about whether or not to use a specific intervention.
>
> **Website:** Please see www.researchautism.net/behavioural-and-developmental-interventions for information about behavioural and developmental interventions including information about specific interventions and details of scientific studies and trials.

Chapter 10:
Behavioural interventions

Introduction

Behavioural interventions are designed to encourage appropriate behaviour (such as getting dressed or talking to other people) and to discourage inappropriate behaviour (such as self-harm or aggression towards others) (1). Therapists, teachers and parents often break down the desired behaviours into small, achievable tasks which are taught in a very structured manner (2).

Some people think that behavioural interventions can significantly improve the core features of autism such as difficulties in social communication, social interaction and restrictive and stereotyped patterns of behaviour. Furthermore, some people have claimed that behavioural interventions can lead to recovery in some children with autism (1, 3).

In this chapter we will cover applied behaviour analysis, early intensive behavioural interventions, techniques which usually form part of a larger programme of intervention (such as discrete-trial training, incidental teaching and the verbal behaviour approach), pivotal response training, and positive behaviour support.

Evidence

Some high quality evidence shows that the core features of autism are difficulties with social communication and social interaction as well as restrictive and stereotyped patterns of behaviour (4). Resulting behaviours include aggression and self-harm, as well as difficulties in learning appropriate behaviours such as communicating with others, making requests and getting dressed (5).

Some forms of early intensive behavioural interventions may provide some benefits to some young children on the autism spectrum according to a very limited amount of research evidence of sufficiently high quality (6). Pivotal response training may provide some benefits to some children on the autism spectrum according to an extremely limited amount of research evidence of sufficiently high quality (7). Determining the benefits of other forms of behavioural intervention, such as positive behavioural support or the individual techniques used within some forms of early intensive behavioural interventions, is more difficult (8). We must wait for further research of sufficiently high quality to be completed.

NICE guidelines

Behavioural interventions may be appropriate under certain circumstances according to the National Institute for Health and Care Excellence. For example, it recommended the use of structured and predictable training programmes based on behavioural principles for adults with autism who need help with the activities of daily living (9).

It also made recommendations on the use of social communication interventions (some of which use behavioural principles) for children and young people with autism.

'Consider a specific social-communication intervention for the core features of autism in children and young people that includes play-based strategies with parents, carers and teachers to increase joint attention, engagement and reciprocal communication in the child or young person. Strategies should:

- be adjusted to the child or young person's developmental level
- aim to increase the parents', carers', teachers' or peers' understanding of, and sensitivity and responsiveness to, the child or young person's patterns of communication and interaction
- include techniques of therapist modelling and video-interaction feedback
- include techniques to expand the child or young person's communication, interactive play and social routines.

The intervention should be delivered by a trained professional. For pre-school children consider parent, carer or teacher mediation. For school-aged children consider peer mediation.' (10)

Choosing Autism Interventions: A Research-Based Guide © Research Autism and Autism West Midlands

Supply, quality and regulation

Some behavioural interventions are delivered by teachers and therapists, others are delivered by parents and carers. Some qualifications and credentials exist for some providers of some forms of behavioural intervention. Some providers, such as teachers, have regulating bodies.

Costs and time

Costs: the costs of a behavioural intervention will depend largely on the programme used, the amount of time needed and the people involved in delivering the intervention. Training and equipment may also be needed. Due to the amount of time and the intensity of some behavioural interventions, costs can reach up to £45,000 a year (11).

Time: some guidelines for behavioural interventions advocate that the intervention is most effective when it is delivered intensively – for 40 hours a week. However, others have suggested that 15–20 hours a week is suitable (12).

Risks and safety

There are no known risks for most forms of behavioural interventions.

Specific forms of behavioural intervention

Applied behaviour analysis

Introduction

Applied behaviour analysis (also known as ABA) is a systematic way of observing someone's behaviour, identifying desirable changes in that behaviour and then using the most appropriate methods to make those changes.

It is based on the idea that someone's behaviour can be changed by altering what happens before the behaviour occurs (known as the antecedent) and/or by altering what happens after the behaviour occurs (known as the consequence).

So, for example, an ABA therapist may try to improve a child's communication and social skills (the behaviour) by demonstrating more effective ways to interact with other children (the antecedent) and then rewarding him (the consequence) when he demonstrates the improved behaviours.

The therapist will then analyse how well that approach has worked and, if necessary, make changes to the intervention to improve the child's behaviour next time around (13).

The principles of ABA are incorporated within many specific interventions, such as discrete-trial training, incidental teaching and pivotal response training (14). These principles are also incorporated in many forms of early intensive behavioural intervention (EIBI) — such as the University of California at Los Angeles Young Autism Project model.

Applied behaviour analysis (ABA)

Definition: a systematic way of observing someone's behaviour, identifying desirable changes in that behaviour and then using the most appropriate methods to make those changes.

Aims: encourage meaningful and important behaviours.

Who: people with autism, including children and adults.

Evidence: assessing possible benefits is difficult due to the wide range of practices.

Risks: none.

Aims

ABA is designed to help a wide range of people, including children and adults on the autism spectrum, as well as individuals with other disabilities.

ABA aims to encourage meaningful and important behaviours in people with autism such as developing basic skills (looking, listening, imitating) and more complex skills (reading, understanding the perspective of others).

The supporters of ABA claim that it can make a meaningful difference to people's lives by not only targeting the core features but also a variety of other behaviours such as self-harm and aggression (15, 16, 17).

Evidence

Determining if ABA has any benefits for individuals on the spectrum is difficult because it includes such a wide range of practices, each of which has different research evidence (18). However, later in this book we assess the evidence for the individual practices which may form part of ABA.

Risks

No risks are known for ABA.

Additional information

ABA has been heavily criticised by some people and continues to be a point of contention among autism researchers, parents, professionals and people with autism. Please visit the Research Autism website for a more detailed overview of the criticisms (18).

Early intensive behavioural interventions

Introduction

Early intensive behavioural interventions (EIBIs) are comprehensive, multi-component packages which use a wide range of behavioural techniques and which are aimed at pre-school children on the autism spectrum. EIBIs are sometimes referred to as 'ABA' because they are based on the principles of applied behaviour analysis. The original and probably best-known of the EIBI programmes is the University of California at Los Angeles Young Autism Project model (UCLA YAP model, also known as the Lovaas method). Here we will describe the evidence for the UCLA YAP model.

Early intensive behavioural interventions – the UCLA YAP model

Definition: intensive interventions where desired behaviours are reinforced and negative behaviours are not reinforced.

Aims: to build positive behaviours such as language and socialisation and suppress unwanted behaviours such as aggression and self-harm.

Who: very young children with autism — high-functioning children seem to respond the most.

Evidence: very limited amount of research evidence that the UCLA YAP model may provide some benefits.

Risks: none.

The UCLA YAP model is based on the idea that autistic children struggle to understand and to communicate with other people and react to such frustrations with tantrums and other challenging behaviour. So the therapy team constructs a teaching environment that is designed to maximise the child's success and minimise failure. Desired behaviour, such as the use of language or social or self-help skills, is positively reinforced and accompanied by lots of praise. Negative behaviour, such as self-harm or aggression towards others, is not reinforced (1).

The UCLA YAP model uses a variety of specific teaching methods including play, natural environment training and incidental teaching (11). The therapists may also use a wide range of other interventions, such as sign language and PECS to suit the needs of the individual child.

Aims

The supporters of the UCLA YAP model (as with other EIBIs) recommend that the intervention should begin as early as possible, preferably before the child is five years old and, ideally, before the child reaches three-and-a-half years old (11). Some supporters also suggest that higher-functioning children (those with higher IQs and language skills) are most likely to benefit (3).

The aim of the intervention is to build positive behaviours such as language and socialisation, and to suppress unwanted behaviours such as self-stimulatory and aggressive behaviours.

In his original study, Lovaas claimed that 47% of the children treated by his method functioned normally and were able to attend mainstream school by the age of five. He also claimed that a further 40% of the children made substantial progress but still displayed autistic characteristics. In addition, he claimed that those children who followed the programme for two years or more gained an average of 30 IQ points compared with the other groups in his study who made no IQ gains (3).

Evidence

EIBI programmes such as the UCLA YAP model may provide some benefits for some individuals on the autism spectrum according to a very limited amount of research evidence of sufficiently high quality.

Individual response to treatment is variable and these programmes do not result in improvements in all areas of functioning. For some children, alternative interventions such as specialist pre-school placements may produce comparable results and may offer greater opportunity for interaction with peers. Considering the benefits of EIBI is important. Compare them to the possible impact on parents (time, finances, organisation and involvement with other siblings). A thorough reward assessment should always be undertaken as many children with autism do not find verbal praise, clapping or touching to be rewarding (6, 19–21).

Risks

No risks are known for EIBI.

Additional information

EIBI is subject to the same criticisms as ABA as a whole.

Techniques which usually form part of a larger programme of interventions

Introduction

Comprehensive, multi-component interventions such as the UCLA YAP model consist of a number of techniques which are combined in different ways for different types of interventions. Here we review three of the main techniques used in large intervention programmes: discrete-trial training, incidental teaching and the verbal behaviour approach.

Discrete-trial training (DTT) is a highly structured training technique where a trainer instructs a person with autism in a series of short lessons (known as 'trials'). Each trial has a definite beginning and end, which is why the trials are described as discrete. The trainer begins each trial with a short, clear instruction or a question. The trainer may also prompt the learner, showing them how to respond correctly to the instruction or question. If the learner does what the trainer wants, the trainer will immediately reward the learner (for example by praising them or allowing them to have something they want). If the learner does not do what the trainer wants, they will repeat the instruction or try a slightly different approach (22).

> ## Discrete-trial training (DTT), incidental teaching and the verbal behaviour approach
>
> **Definition:** techniques which usually form part of larger programmes of intervention.
>
> **Aims:** to improve a range of behaviours including social communication and social interaction.
>
> **Who:** mainly children with autism.
>
> **Evidence:** weak evidence suggests there may be some benefits when these techniques are used alone.
>
> **Risks:** none.

Incidental teaching is where a teacher takes advantage of a naturally occurring situation (an incident) to provide a lesson for the student. It is based on the idea that students, including children with autism, are more willing to learn if the teaching is centred on their own interests and preferences. In incidental teaching the teacher organises the learning environment around a set of pre-planned learning objectives but takes into account the student's individual preferences. When the student demonstrates an interest in an item or activity, the teacher encourages that interest by questioning or prompting the student. For example, the teacher may place something that the student wants just out of reach so that the student has to communicate with the teacher to get it (23).

The verbal behaviour approach is based on the idea that learning language to request an item is very different to learning language to acknowledge or name an item. It suggests that students must learn the different uses of language separately to be able to communicate effectively. The verbal behaviour approach describes the different types of language as mands (requests), tacts (labels), echoics (repeating or echoing a word) and intraverbals (a response to what someone else is saying, such as the answer to a question). The supporters of the verbal behaviour approach think that teaching mands should be the first priority as this can lead to improvements in other areas (24).

Aims

These techniques are most commonly used for children with autism because they tend to form part of early intensive behavioural interventions. However they can also be used for adults with autism.

The main aim of these techniques tends to be to improve communication. In particular, the verbal behaviour approach aims to help children to use language.

Some people claim that these techniques can help to improve communication skills, which can lead to learning other skills such as dressing, eating, making a bed and improve quality of life (22–24).

Evidence

Specific behavioural techniques such as these may provide some benefits for individuals on the autism spectrum when used alone but the quality of the evidence is weak. However, some of these techniques may provide some benefits to young children with autism when used within EIBI programmes, such as the UCLA YAP model, according to a very limited amount of research evidence of sufficiently high quality (6).

Risks

No risks are known for any of these techniques.

Pivotal response training

Introduction

Pivotal response training (PRT) is based on the idea that certain aspects of a child's development are crucial ('pivotal') for the behaviours which depend on them. The pivotal areas are motivation, self-management, self-initiation, and the ability to respond to multiple environmental cues. PRT is a form of teaching in which the teacher concentrates on changing these pivotal behaviours in order to change the behaviours which depend on them, such as speech and language, social behaviour and challenging behaviour (14).

Pivotal response training

Definition: a form of teaching in which a teacher focuses on changing 'pivotal' areas in order to change behaviours that depend on these, such as speech and language, social behaviour and challenging behaviour.

Aims: to improve social skills, adaptive functioning and communication.

Who: young children with autism.

Evidence: extremely limited amount of research evidence that pivotal response training may provide some benefits.

Risks: none.

Aims

PRT is mainly used in younger children with autism, although it can be used with older people.

Some supporters of PRT claim that it can be used to teach language, decrease challenging behaviour and increase social and communication skills (28, 29).

Evidence

PRT may provide some benefits for some individuals on the autism spectrum according to an extremely limited amount of research evidence of sufficiently high quality (7).

Risks

No risks are known for PRT.

Additional information

There are several multi-component programmes (such as the Early Start Denver Model and the Nova Scotia early intensive behavioural intervention) which include PRT as a key element.

Positive behaviour support

Introduction

Positive behaviour support (PBS) is a process in which individuals are assisted in acquiring helpful, socially meaningful behaviours and encouraged to overcome unhelpful behaviours. PBS plans typically change existing environments, removing triggering events (for example loud noises) in a manner that makes problem behaviours irrelevant, ineffective and inefficient.

An important component of PBS is a functional behavioural assessment. This provides information about the function of problem behaviours. The therapist can then put together plans that are positive, educational and functional to remove the problem behaviours (30–31).

Positive behaviour support

Definition: a process in which individuals are assisted in acquiring adaptive, socially meaningful behaviours and encouraged to overcome unhelpful behaviours.

Aims: to teach functional skills as a replacement for problem behaviour.

Who: people with autism of all ages and abilities.

Evidence: insufficient evidence to determine if PBS has any benefits.

Risks: none.

Aims

PBS is designed for use with people on the autism spectrum of all ages and abilities.

The aim of PBS is to teach functional skills as a replacement for problem behaviour.

Some people claim that PBS can reduce behaviour problems and also enhance a person's quality of life by enabling the person to access the community, form relationships and make choices (30–31).

Evidence

Determining the benefits of PBS for people on the autism spectrum is not currently possible. We must wait for further research of sufficiently high quality to be completed (8).

Risks

No risks are known for PBS.

Further information

In this book: Please see How to use this book (page 11), Chapter 3 (page 38) for information about interventions, Chapter 4 (page 43) for information about how scientists evaluate those interventions, and Section 3 (page 284) for advice on making the decision about whether or not to use a specific intervention.

Website: Please see www.researchautism.net/behavioural-interventions for information about behavioural interventions including information about specific interventions and details of scientific studies and trials.

References

1. IAN Network (2012) *Behavioral Therapies: Key interventions in ASD*. Baltimore, MD: IAN Network.

2. Camargo SPH, Rispoli M, Ganz J, Hong ER, Davis H & Mason R (2014) A review of the quality of behaviorally-based intervention research to improve social interaction dkills of children with ASD in inclusive settings. *Journal of Autism and Developmental Disorders September* **44** (9) 2096–2116.

3. Lovaas O (1987) Behavioral treatment and normal educational and intellectual functioning in young autistic children. *Journal of Consulting and Clinical Psychology* **55** 3–9.

4. American Psychiatric Association (2013) *Diagnostic and Statistical Manual of Mental Disorders – DSM-5*. Washington, D.C: American Psychiatric Association.

5. Westphal A & Volkmar FR (2008) An update on autism. *The Journal of Lifelong Learning in Psychiatry* **6** 284–292.

6. Research Autism (2014) *UCLA YAP Model and autism*. [online]. Available at: www.researchautism.net/ucla-yap-model-and-autism (accessed January 13, 2015).

7. Research Autism (2014) *Pivotal response training and autism*. [online]. Available at: www.researchautism.net/pivotal-response-training-and-autism (accessed January 13, 2015).

8. Research Autism (2014) *Positive behaviour support and autism*. [online]. Available at: www.researchautism.net/positive-behavioural-support (accessed January 13, 2015).

9. National Institute for Health and Care Excellence (2012) *Autism: Recognition, referral, diagnosis and management of adults on the autism spectrum*. London: National Institute for Health and Care Excellence.

10. National Institute for Health and Care Excellence (2013) *The Management and Support of Children and Young People on the Autism Spectrum*. London: National Institute for Health and Care Excellence.

11. Eikeseth S, Hayward D & Gale (2013) *UK Young Autism Project: Programme information*. London: UK Young Autism Project.

12. Smith T (1999) Outcome of early intervention for children With autism. *Clinical Psychology: Science and Practice* **6** (1) pp. 33–49

13. Dixon DR, Vogel T & Tarbox J (2012) A brief history of functional analysis and applied behaviour analysis. In: JL Matson (Ed) *Functional Assessment For Challenging Behaviours*. New York: Springer.

14. IAN Network (2012) *Floortime and Pivotal Response Training*. Baltimore, MD: IAN Network.

15. Maine Administrators of Services for Children with Disabilities (2000) *Report of the MADSEC Autism Task Force (Revised edition)*. Manchester, ME: Maine Administrators of Services for Children with Disabilities.

16. Virués-Ortega J (2010) Applied behavior analytic intervention for autism in early childhood: meta-analysis, meta-regression and dose-response meta-analysis of multiple outcomes. *Clinical Psychology Review* **30** 387–99.

17. Green G, Taylor BA, Luce S & Krantz PJ (2000) *What Does Research Tell Us about ABA and Autism?* New York, NY: Autism Speaks.

18. Research Autism (2014) *Applied behaviour analysis and autism*. [online]. Available at: www.researchautism.net/applied-behaviour-analysis-and-autism (accessed January 13, 2015).

19. Howlin P, Magiati I & Charman T (2009) Systematic review of early intensive behavioral interventions for children with autism. *American Journal of Intellectual and Developmental Disabilities* **114** 23–41.

20. Reichow B, Barton EE, Boyd BA & Hume K (2012) Early intensive behavioral intervention (EIBI) for young children with autism spectrum disorders (ASD). *Cochrane Database of Systematic Reviews* doi: 10.1002/14651858.CD009260.pub2.

21. Eldevik S, Hastings RP, Hughes JC, Jahr E, Eikeseth S & Cross S (2009) Meta-analysis of Early Intensive Behavioral Intervention for children with autism. *Journal of Clinical Child and Adolescent Psychology* **38** 439–450.

22. Smith T (2001) Discrete Trial Training in the Treatment of Autism. *Focus on Autism and Other Developmental Disabilities* **16** 86–92.

23. The Lovaas Institute (2007) *Incidental Teaching Techniques*. Los Angeles, CA: Lovaas Institute.

24. Autism Speaks (2014) *Verbal Behavior Therapy*. New York, NY: Autism Speaks.

25. Research Autism (2014) *Discrete trial training and autism*. [online]. Available at: www.researchautism.net/discrete-trial-training-and-autism (accessed January 13, 2015).

26. Research Autism (2014) *Incidental teaching and autism*. [online]. Available at: www.researchautism.net/incidental-teaching-and-autism (accessed January 13, 2015).

27. Research Autism (2014) *Verbal behaviour approach and autism*. [online]. Available at: www.researchautism.net/verbal-behaviour-approach (accessed January 13, 2015).

28. The UCSB Koegel Autism Centre (2014) *Pivotal Response Treatment*. Available at: https://education.ucsb.edu/autism/pivotal-response-treatment/general-information (accessed February 10, 2015).

29. Baker-Ericzen MJ, Stahmer AC & Burns A (2007) Child demographics associated with outcomes in a community-based pivotal response training program. *Journal of Positive Behavior Interventions* **9** 52–60.

30. Association for Positive Behavior Support (2011) *Brief Description of PBS Related to Autism Spectrum Disorder*. Bloomsburg, PA: Association for Positive Behavior Support.

31. Durand VM, Hieneman M, Clarke S, Wang M & Rinaldi ML (2012) Positive family intervention for severe challenging behavior I: a multisite randomized clinical trial. *Journal of Positive Behavior Interventions* **15** 133–143.

Chapter 11:
Developmental interventions

Introduction

Developmental interventions target the core developmental areas within the individual rather than their outward behaviours.

Developmental interventions are based on the idea that some children have difficulty reaching certain developmental milestones but that they can be helped to meet those milestones through playful, structured interaction with an adult (1).

Therapists, teachers and parents work with the child's own interests or actions to slowly build engagement, interaction, communication, affection, and then specific skills such as logical reasoning and symbolic thinking.

Developmental interventions include the DIR method, intensive interaction, and milieu training. Many other interventions use developmental techniques, such as the Relationship Development Intervention (RDI). Please see Chapter 14 on relationship-based interventions on page 145 for more information.

Evidence

Some high quality evidence shows that children on the autism spectrum have difficulty reaching certain developmental milestones associated with the development of social communication skills and social interaction (2).

Some very limited research evidence shows that some developmental interventions, such as the DIR method and milieu training, may provide some benefits for some children on the autism spectrum. Determining if other developmental interventions, such as intensive interaction, have any benefits is not currently possible. We must wait for further research of sufficiently high quality to be completed (3–5).

NICE guidelines

The National Institute for Health and Care Excellence does not provide specific guidance on the use of developmental interventions in autism.

However, it did make the following recommendations on the use of social communication interventions (some of which use developmental principles) for children and young people with autism (6):

'Consider a specific social-communication intervention for the core features of autism in children and young people that includes play-based strategies with parents, carers and teachers to increase joint attention, engagement and reciprocal communication in the child or young person. Strategies should:

- be adjusted to the child or young person's developmental level
- aim to increase the parents', carers', teachers' or peers' understanding of, and sensitivity and responsiveness to, the child or young person's patterns of communication and interaction
- include techniques of therapist modelling and video-interaction feedback
- include techniques to expand the child or young person's communication, interactive play and social routines.

The intervention should be delivered by a trained professional. For pre-school children consider parent, carer or teacher mediation. For school-aged children consider peer mediation.'

Supply, quality and regulation

Some developmental interventions are delivered by parents and carers, others are delivered by teachers and therapists.

No internationally recognised qualifications or credentials exist for providers of most developmental interventions. Some providers (for example teachers) have regulating bodies.

Costs and time

Costs: the cost of a developmental intervention depends on the programme used. Training and materials may be additional costs.

For example, one study suggested that the average cost of the DIR method is $2,500 (approximately £1,250) a year, although the exact costs will likely depend on the specific needs of the individual child and the level of service provided by the programme suppliers (7).

Time: the time will vary depending on the person with autism and the programme used. For example, children using the DIR method get three to five hours of treatment, which is provided in 8–10 sessions of 20–30 minute sessions each throughout the day (7).

Risks and safety

No risks are known for most developmental interventions.

Specific forms of developmental intervention

DIR method

Introduction

The DIR method (also known as Floortime, DIR Floortime or the Developmental, Individual Difference, Relationship-Based Model) is a comprehensive, multi-component intervention used to help children with autism and other developmental disabilities. It is based on the idea that some children have difficulty reaching certain developmental milestones (such as communication and motor skills) and that through playful, structured interaction with an adult these milestones can be reached. The key technique used within the DIR method is

---

DIR method

Definition: an intervention which consists of a series of 'Floortime' exercises in which the carer takes an active role in spontaneous and fun activities that are directed by the child's interests and actions.

Aims: to master missed developmental milestones (in communication and motor skills for example).

Who: young children with autism.

Evidence: extremely limited amount of research evidence that the DIR method may provide some benefits.

Risks: none.

a series of 'Floortime' exercises in which the carer takes an active role in spontaneous and fun activities that are directed by the child's interests and actions (8).

Aims

The DIR method was designed for infants, toddlers and pre-schoolers with autism but it can also be used with older children.

According to the Floortime Foundation, the aim of the DIR method is to master the milestones that were missed in early development.

The Floortime Foundation claim that the DIR method can help children with autism to become 'warm, engaged and loving', active learners and able to attend mainstream school (9).

Evidence

The DIR method may provide some benefits for some individuals on the autism spectrum according to an extremely limited amount of research evidence of sufficiently high quality (3).

Risks and safety

No risks are known for the DIR method.

Intensive interaction

Introduction

Intensive interaction is based on natural conversations at a level that the person can understand and join in with. This is achieved by following the individual's lead and mirroring their behaviours and vocalisations. Once an individual's attention has been gained a sequence of interactions begin, building over time. During the interactions the individual learns the fundamentals of communication (getting a response and responding, reading and using facial expressions, body language, eye contact, turn-taking, vocalising) (10).

Aims

The main aim of intensive interaction is to teach the fundamentals of communication to people with autism, learning difficulties, or both. One of the most important things an individual learns through the process is that other people are good to be with and that other people enjoy being with them (10).

Evidence

Determining the benefits of intensive interaction for developing communication skills in people with autism is not currently possible. We must wait for further research of sufficiently high quality to be completed (5).

Risks and safety

No risks are associated with intensive interaction.

Intensive interaction

Definition: an approach based on natural conversations at a level that the person can understand and join in with.

Aims: to learn the fundamentals of communication.

Who: children and adults with autism or learning difficulties or both.

Evidence: insufficient evidence to determine if intensive interaction has any benefits.

Risks: none.

Milieu training

Introduction

The teacher in milieu training takes advantage of the child's interest in the things around them (the 'milieu') to provide learning opportunities for the child. When the child demonstrates an interest in an item or activity, the teacher encourages that interest by questioning or prompting the student. For example, the teacher may place something that the student wants just out of reach, so that the student has to communicate with the teacher to get it (11).

Aims

Milieu training is mainly aimed at children with autism but may be appropriate for any person at the early stages of language development.

The aim of milieu training is to increase and improve communication skills (11).

Some people claim that as well as improving communication skills, milieu training can reduce problem behaviours (12).

Milieu training

Definition: teaching where the teacher takes advantage of the child's interest in the things around them to provide learning opportunities.

Aims: to increase and improve communication skills.

Who: children with autism.

Evidence: very limited amount of research evidence that milieu training may provide some benefits.

Risks: none.

Evidence

Milieu training may provide some benefits for some individuals on the autism spectrum according to a very limited amount of research evidence of sufficiently high quality (4).

Risks and safety

No risks are known for milieu training.

Further information

In this book: Please see How to use this book (page 11), Chapter 3 (page 38) for information about interventions, Chapter 4 (page 43) for information about how scientists evaluate those interventions, and Section 3 (page 284) for advice on making the decision about whether or not to use a specific intervention.

Website: Please see www.researchautism.net/developmental-interventions for information about developmental interventions including information about specific interventions and details of scientific studies and trials.

References

1. IAN Network (2007) *Educational and Behavioural Therapies*. Baltimore, MD: IAN Network.

2. American Psychiatric Association (2013) *Diagnostic and Statistical Manual of Mental Disorders: DSM-5*. Washington, D.C: American Psychiatric Association.

3. Research Autism (2014) *DIR Method and autism* [online]. Available at: www.researchautism.net/dir-method-and-autism (accessed January 13, 2015).

4. Research Autism (2014) *Intensive interaction and autism* [online]. Available at: www.researchautism.net/intensive-interaction (accessed January 13, 2015).

5. Research Autism (2014) *Milieu training and autism* [online]. Available at: www.researchautism.net/milieu-training-and-autism (accessed January 13, 2015).

6. National Institute for Health and Care Excellence (2013) *The Management and Support of Children and Young People on the Autism Spectrum*. London: National Institute for Health and Care Excellence.

7. Solomon R, Necheles J, Ferch C & Bruckman D (2007) Pilot study of a parent training program for young children with autism: the PLAY Project Home Consultation program. *Autism: The International Journal of Research and Practice* **11** 205–24.

8. IAN Network (2012) *Floortime and Pivotal Response Training*. Baltimore, MD: IAN Network.

9. Interdisciplinary Council on Development and Learning (2014) *DIR Floortime*. Available at: www.icdl.com (accessed 16 January 2015).

10. Caldwell P (2006) Speaking the other's language: Imitation as a gateway to relationship. *Infant and Child Development* **15** 275–282.

11. Christensen-Sandfort RJ & Whinnery SB (2011) Impact of milieu teaching on communication skills of young children with autism spectrum disorder. *Topics in Early Childhood Special Education* **32** 211–222.

12. Mancil GR, Conroy MA & Haydon TF (2009) Effects of a modified milieu therapy intervention on the social communicative behaviors of young children with autism spectrum disorders. *Journal of Autism and Developmental Disorders* **39** 149–63.

Chapter 12:
Comprehensive, multi-component approaches

Introduction

Comprehensive, multi-component approaches are made of a mixture of techniques, many borrowed from behavioural or developmental interventions. They may be delivered by parents, teachers or a combination of parents and teachers.

Some comprehensive, multi-component approaches use a wide range of techniques to target a specific range of behaviours or developmental areas. For example, the SCERTS model is designed to target 'Social Communication, Emotional Regulation and Transactional Support'. By contrast, TEACCH uses a set of techniques known as structured teaching to target a range of behavioural and developmental issues.

In practice, many behavioural and developmental interventions found elsewhere in this book (such as some forms of early intensive behavioural intervention) are comprehensive, multi-component approaches. Here we focus on those comprehensive, multi-component interventions not covered elsewhere in this book: the SCERTS model, the SPELL framework and the TEACCH model (2, 3, 4).

Evidence

Some high-quality evidence shows that people with autism have difficulties with the core features of autism such as difficulties with social communication and social interaction, restrictive, repetitive and stereotyped patterns of behaviour and sensory issues (1).

The evidence for the effectiveness of comprehensive, multi-component approaches is mixed. For example, some approaches, such as TEACCH, may provide some benefits to some individuals on the autism spectrum according to a limited amount of research evidence of sufficiently high quality. Determining the benefits of other approaches, such as SCERTS or SPELL, is not possible. We must wait for further research of sufficiently high quality to be completed (2–4).

NICE guidelines

The National Institute for Health and Care Excellence reported on a study of LEAP, a comprehensive, multi-component approach used in the USA but not currently available in the UK (5):

'There is evidence from one moderate-sized trial that adequately supervised comprehensive programmes can help manage the core symptoms of autism and co-existing difficulties. However, the quality of the trial was low.'

Supply, quality and regulation

Comprehensive, multi-component approaches may be delivered by parents and carers, by professionals, or by both.

Some qualifications and credentials are available for some providers of some forms of comprehensive, multi-component approaches. Some regulating bodies exist for some providers, such as teachers, but no internationally recognised qualifications are specific to the approaches we describe here.

Costs and time

Costs: the costs of comprehensive, multi-component approaches will depend largely on the approach and the specific techniques used. The major cost is likely to be the time of the person delivering the intervention, although things like training, travel, accommodation, materials and equipment are also necessary for most approaches.

Time: the time required will vary depending on the specific techniques being used within each approach and on the needs and abilities of the individual with autism. In theory, some of these approaches are designed to be used throughout the day throughout someone's lifetime.

No risks are known for most forms of comprehensive, multi-component approaches.

Specific forms of comprehensive, multi-component programmes

SCERTS

Introduction

The Social Communication, Emotional Regulation and Transactional Support (SCERTS) model aims to directly address core developmental areas in the individual child with autism.

It addresses key areas such as social communication, social relatedness and sensory characteristics, as well as providing support to the individual and to the family. Practitioners following the model use a combination of techniques and strategies to meet the specific needs of the individual child, many of them borrowed from other interventions (6, 7).

> **SCERTS**
>
> **Definition:** a model that focuses on social communication, emotional regulation and transactional support.
>
> **Aims:** to help children become social communicators while preventing behaviours which may interfere with learning and relationships.
>
> **Who:** mainly children with autism, but theoretically suitable for adults.
>
> **Evidence:** insufficient evidence to determine if SCERTS has any benefits as a whole but some of the individual components are evidence-based.
>
> **Risks:** none.

Aims

SCERTS was designed for children but the model is applicable to adults.

The aim of SCERTS is to help children become social communicators while preventing behaviours which may interfere with learning and relationships.

Some people think that the child-centred approach of SCERTS facilitates the development of functional social communication, emotion regulation and coping strategies (6, 7).

Evidence

Determining the benefits of the SCERTS model for children with autism is not currently possible. We must wait for further research of sufficiently high quality to be completed. However, many of the components used in SCERTS are claimed to be evidence-based and the intervention is child-centred, which means that different evidence-based components are used for different children (2).

Risks

No risks are known for SCERTS.

SPELL

Introduction

The National Autistic Society developed the SPELL framework for understanding and responding to the needs of children and adults on the autism spectrum. SPELL stands for Structure, Positive (approaches and expectations), Empathy, Low-Arousal, and Links. It aims to identify underlying issues, reducing the disabling effects of the condition, and in providing a cornerstone for communication. It also forms the basis of all autism-specific staff training (8).

SPELL

Definition: a framework developed by the National Autistic Society for understanding and responding to the needs of children and adults on the autism spectrum.

Aims: to understand and respond to the needs of people on the spectrum.

Who: people with autism of all ages and abilities.

Evidence: insufficient evidence to determine if SPELL has any benefits as a whole but some of the individual components are evidence-based.

Risks: none.

Aims

The SPELL framework is targeted at supporting all people with autism. The aim is to understand and respond to the needs of children and adults on the autism spectrum. Some people claim that by building on strengths and reducing the disabling effects of the condition, progress can be made in personal growth and development, the promotion of opportunity and as full a life as possible (8).

Evidence

Determining the benefits of the SPELL framework for people with autism is not currently possible. We must wait for further research of sufficiently high quality to be completed. However, many of the components used in SPELL are claimed to be evidence-based themselves and the intervention is person-centred meaning that different evidence-based components are used for different individuals (3).

Risks

No risks are associated with SPELL.

TEACCH

Introduction

TEACCH (Treatment and Education of Autistic and Communication-handicapped children) describes various activities undertaken by Division TEACCH, a state-wide community-based programme of services for children and adults in North Carolina, USA. The TEACCH approach is based on understanding the culture of autism – the characteristic patterns of thinking and behaviour seen in individuals with autism. It is also based around developing an individualised person-centred (and family-centred) plan for each client or student, rather than a standard curriculum. TEACCH is designed to make the most of an individual's strengths within a structured environment – sometimes known as 'structured teaching'.

The four major components of structured teaching are physical structure (the organisation of the room), visual schedules (visual information depicting where, when and what the activity will be), work systems (visual information telling an individual what to do while in a work or play area), and task organisation (visually clear information on what the task is about). Elements of the TEACCH approach are used extensively alongside other approaches within other multi-component interventions throughout the work, such as SPELL (9, 10).

TEACCH

Definition: an approach based on understanding the characteristic patterns of thinking and behaviour seen in individuals with autism.

Aims: to help to prepare people with autism for living and working more effectively.

Who: people with autism of all ages and abilities and their families.

Evidence: limited amount of research evidence that TEACCH may provide some benefits.

Risks: none.

Aims

The primary aim of TEACCH is to help to prepare people with autism to live or work more effectively at home, at school and in the community.

The TEACCH approach is used with people on the autism spectrum of all ages and abilities and their families.

Some people claim that TEACCH can lead to improvements in areas such as intellectual abilities, adaptive behaviours that are key for daily living, and social skills (9, 10).

Evidence

The TEACCH approach and structured teaching may provide some benefits for some individuals on the autism spectrum according to a very limited amount of research evidence of sufficiently high quality (4). Determining the benefits of the individual components of structured teaching (such as visual schedules) for individuals on the autism spectrum is not currently possible. We must wait for further research of sufficiently high quality to be completed.

Risks

No risks are known for TEACCH.

Further information

In this book: Please see How to use this book (page 11), Chapter 3 (page 38) for information about interventions, Chapter 4 (page 43) for information about how scientists evaluate those interventions, and Section 3 (page 284) for advice on making the decision about whether or not to use a specific intervention.

Websites: Please see www.researchautism.net/comprehensive-multicomponent-interventions for information about comprehensive, multi-component approaches including information about specific approaches and details of scientific studies and trials.

References

1. American Psychiatric Association (2013) *Diagnostic and Statistical Manual of Mental Disorders – DSM-5*. Washington, D.C: American Psychiatric Association.

2. Research Autism (2014) *SCERTS and autism* [online]. Available at: www.researchautism.net/scerts (accessed January 13, 2015).

3. Research Autism (2014) *SPELL model* [online]. Available at: www.researchautism.net/spell (accessed January 13, 2015).

4. Research Autism (2014) *TEACCH and autism* [online]. Available at: www.researchautism.net/teacch-and-autism (accessed January 13, 2015).

5. National Institute for Health and Care Excellence (2013) *The Management and Support of Children and Young People on the Autism Spectrum*. London: National Institute for Health and Care Excellence.

6. Prizant BM, Wetherby AM, Rubin E & Laurent AC (2010) *The SCERTS Model and Evidence-Based Practice*. Available at: www.scerts.com/docs/SCERTS_EBP 090810 v1.pdf (accessed 19 January, 2015).

7. O'Neill J, Bergstrand L, Bowman K, Elliott K, Mavin L, Stephenson S & Wayman C (2010) The SCERTS model: implementation and evaluation in a primary special school. *Good Autism Practice* **11** 7–15.

8. National Autistic Society (2014) *SPELL*. London: National Autistic Society.

9. Mesibov GB & Shea V (2010) The TEACCH program in the era of evidence-based practice. *Journal of Autism and Developmental Disorders* **40** 570–9.

10. Virues-Ortega J, Julio FM & Pastor-Barriuso R (2013) The TEACCH program for children and adults with autism: a meta-analysis of intervention studies. *Clinical Psychology Review* **33** 940–53.

Chapter 13:
Parent training and support programmes

Introduction

The term 'parent training and support programme' is very wide-ranging and means different things to different people. In practice, it means any programme in which parents (or carers) are taught how to help their own children or supported in other ways. The emphasis in these programmes is both on improving parental confidence and mental health and on changing the child's behaviour (1).

Parent training and support programmes overlap with other types of intervention, especially behavioural and developmental interventions, because most parent training and support programmes use one or more behavioural or developmental techniques. For example, the DIR method (see page 125) and some forms of early intensive behavioural intervention (see page 112) involve parent training and support.

We focus on some of the most commonly used parent training and support programmes used in the UK and which we don't cover elsewhere. This includes the Barnardo's Cygnet programme, the National Autistic Society's EarlyBird programmes, and Portage.

Evidence

A significant amount of evidence shows that many parents (and other carers) find looking after children on the autism spectrum very challenging, although many also say they find significant benefits (2).

Some parent training and support programmes (such as the DIR method and some forms of early intensive behavioural interventions) covered elsewhere this book have some supporting research evidence. Less evidence exists for the interventions in this chapter.

NICE guidelines

The National Institute for Health and Care Excellence does not provide guidance on the use of parent training and support programmes in autism. However it does recommend that:

'When the needs of families and carers have been identified, discuss help available locally and, taking into account their preferences, offer information, advice, training and support, especially if they:

'are involved in the delivery of an intervention for the child or young person in collaboration with health and social care professionals.' (3)

Supply, quality and regulation

Some parent training and support interventions are delivered by professionals, such as teachers and psychologists, while others are delivered by staff of voluntary organisations. In practice, many parent training and support services, such as the NAS EarlyBird programme, are only available to parents in certain areas of the UK because of resource constraints.

Some qualifications and credentials are available for some providers of parent training and support interventions. For example, Portage home visitors are trained by the National Portage Association (4).

Costs and time

Costs: the cost of parent training and support interventions will depend on the programme. In practice, many interventions are free to parents at the point of delivery, although they may have to pay for additional elements such as any travel, accommodation and materials.

Time: the time will vary depending on the parents, the child and the programme. For example, an NAS EarlyBird programme lasts 'for three months and combines group training sessions with individual home visits, when video feedback is used to help parents apply what they've learnt. Parents will have a weekly commitment of a two-and-a-half hour training session or home visit, and to ongoing work with their child at home.' (5)

Risks and safety

No risks are known for most forms of parent training and support programmes.

Specific parent training and support programmes

Barnardo's Cygnet programme

Introduction

The Barnardo's Cygnet model is based on the Parent Adviser Model, which was developed to support families of disabled children.

The model came from parents' concerns that they were not being listened to by professionals, who they felt focused almost exclusively on the management of children's problems, without taking account of their adaptation to difficult situations.

> **Barnado's Cygnet programme**
>
> **Definition:** a six-week programme aimed at families of children on the autism spectrum.
>
> **Aims:** to build on parents' knowledge and experiences.
>
> **Who:** parents of children with autism aged between seven and 18.
>
> **Evidence:** no evidence to suggest that the Cygnet programme provides any benefits to parents or children.
>
> **Risks:** none.

The Barnardo's Cygnet programme is delivered in a group format, and each session is designed to help participants examine a specific issue (such as diagnosis, communication, sensory issues and challenging behaviours) (6).

Aims

The Barnardo's Cygnet programme is aimed at families of children on the autism spectrum aged seven to 18.

It builds a mutually supportive environment in which parents and carers learn about autism, learn about behaviours, learn strategies for managing difficult behaviours, and are signposted to relevant resources.

Choosing Autism Interventions: A Research-Based Guide © Research Autism and Autism West Midlands

Some people claim that the programme can help parents increase their own sense of competence and enable them to improve some behaviours in their children (6).

Evidence

No research evidence of sufficiently high quality shows that the Barnardo's Cygnet programme provides any benefits to families of children on the autism spectrum. We must wait for further research of sufficiently high quality to be completed (7).

Risks and safety

No risks are known for the Barnardo's Cygnet programme.

NAS EarlyBird programme

Introduction

The National Autistic Society EarlyBird programme is aimed at families of pre-school children. The EarlyBird Plus programme is aimed at families of children aged four to eight.

The programmes combine group training sessions for parents and individual home visits where video feedback is used. The feedback helps parents apply what they learnt, while they are working with their child.

The programmes use techniques from other interventions such as the NAS SPELL Framework, TEACCH and PECS (5, 8).

NAS EarlyBird programme

Definition: a three-month programme aimed at families of young children.

Aims: to support parents and to help them facilitate appropriate communication and behaviour in their children.

Who: parents of preschool children, or children aged four to eight, with autism.

Evidence: insufficient evidence to determine if the NAS EarlyBird programme has any benefits for parents or children.

Risks: none.

Aims

The NAS EarlyBird programme is designed for parents of newly diagnosed children of pre-school age. It aims to support parents in the period between diagnosis and school placement.

Some people claim that the programme can help parents to improve their child's communication and appropriate behaviour and pre-empts the development of inappropriate behaviour (5, 8).

Evidence

Determining any improvements in children of parents who participate in EarlyBird programmes is not currently possible. We must wait for further research of sufficiently high quality to be completed (9).

Risks and safety

No risks are known for the NAS EarlyBird programme.

Portage

Introduction

Portage is an early childhood service that aims to support families in their own homes who have young children with additional needs.

The children are taught new skills through the use of questions and tasks, prompts, and rewards. Parents and carers are shown how to apply this system by a weekly or fortnightly visit from a Portage home visitor (4).

Portage

Definition: an early childhood service that supports families in their own homes.

Aims: to teach children new skills through the use of questions and tasks, prompts and rewards.

Who: parents of children with special educational needs.

Evidence: insufficient research evidence to determine if Portage has any benefits.

Risks: none.

Aims and claims

Portage is designed to help families with pre-school children with special educational needs. This includes children who have profound and multiple learning difficulties, children with complex social communication difficulties, autism, and children with challenging behaviour (4).

Evidence

Determining the benefits of Portage for individuals on the autism spectrum is not currently possible. We must wait for further research of sufficiently high quality to be completed. Portage may provide some limited benefits to those families, especially when it is adapted for use with children on the autism spectrum, according to the research evidence that does exist. However, Portage may not provide as many benefits to families with children on the autism spectrum as other early interventions according to the research evidence (10).

Risks and safety

No risks are known for portage.

Further information

In this book: Please see How to use this book (page 11), Chapter 3 (page 38) for information about interventions, Chapter 4 (page 43) for information about how scientists evaluate those interventions, and Section 3 (page 284) for advice on making the decision about whether or not to use a specific intervention.

Websites: Please see www.researchautism.net/parent-training-and-support for information about parent-training and support programmes including information about specific programmes and details of scientific studies and trials.

References

1. Oono I, Honey EJ & McConachie H (2013) Parent-mediated early intervention for young children with autism spectrum disorders (ASD) (Review). *Cochrane Database of Systematic Reviews* **4** CD009774.

2. Myers BJ, Mackintosh VH & Goin-Kochel RP (2009) 'My greatest joy and my greatest heart ache': parents' own words on how having a child in the autism spectrum has affected their lives and their families' lives. *Research in Autism Spectrum Disorders* **3** 670–684.

3. National Institute for Health and Care Excellence (2013) *The Management and Support of Children and Young People on the Autism Spectrum*. London: National Institute for Health and Care Excellence.

4. National Portage Association (2000) *Parents FAQ*. Birmingham: National Portage Association.

5. National Autistic Society (2013) *EarlyBird*. London: National Autistic Society.

6. Barnardo's (2013) *Cygnet for Parents: Trainer's guide*. Romford, Essex: Barnardo's.

7. Research Autism (2014) *Barnardo's Cygnet programme and autism* [online]. Available at: www.researchautism.net/barnardo-cygnet-programme (accessed January 13, 2015).

8. Shields J (2000) The NAS EarlyBird Programme: autism-specific early intervention for parents. *Professional Care of Mother and Child* **10** 53–54.

9. Research Autism (2014) *NAS EarlyBird programme and autism* [online]. Available at: www.researchautism.net/nas-early-bird-programme (accessed January 13, 2015).

10. Research Autism (2014) *Portage and autism* [online]. Available at: www.researchautism.net/portage-and-autism (accessed January 13, 2015).

Chapter 14:
Relationship-based interventions

Introduction

Relationship-based interventions focus on the individual's ability to form positive, meaningful relationships with other people.

The aim of most relationship-based interventions is to build relationships within the family, meaning that all family members (not just the person on the autism spectrum) learn how to interact with other family members.

Most relationship-based interventions use a range of techniques. For example, the RDI programme uses a combination of behavioural and developmental techniques. Other relationship-based interventions, such as family therapy, use one or more techniques used in psychological interventions (1).

Here we look at relationship-based interventions which use behavioural and developmental techniques. For relationship-based interventions which use psychological techniques, please see Chapter 22 on psychological therapies on page 238.

Evidence

Some evidence shows that some individuals on the autism spectrum and their parents and carers struggle to form positive, meaningful relationships with each other (2).

Determining the benefits of relationship-based interventions for people on the autism spectrum or their parents (or carers) and other family members is not currently possible. We must wait for further research of sufficiently high quality to be completed (3–5).

NICE guidelines

The National Institute for Health and Care Excellence does not provide specific guidance on the use of relationship-based interventions. However, it does recommend that strategies should: 'aim to increase the parents', carers', teachers' or peers' understanding of, and sensitivity and responsiveness to, the child or young person's patterns of communication and interaction' which is a core element in some (but not all) relationship-based interventions (6).

Supply, quality and regulation

The relationship-based interventions we describe here are usually delivered by parents or carers since the development of the relationship is a core aim of the treatment.

A number of organisations offer various forms of support to family members. For example, the Autism Treatment Center of America, which developed the Son-Rise Program, sells a wide range of support including residential courses, books, DVDs, CDs and telephone consultations. It also offers a limited number of free services and some financial support for those who cannot afford its services.

No internationally recognised qualifications or accreditation programmes are available for the providers or support organisations of most relationship-based interventions.

Costs and time

Costs: the costs of relationship-based interventions will depend on the programme used. For example, the costs of holding therapy are relatively minor since the major cost is the parent's own time. However, some relationship-based programmes have significant additional costs such as training, travel, accommodation and materials. For example, one parent from Norway estimated that he had spent more than $18,000 implementing the Son-Rise Program in the first year (excluding foreign travel) (7).

Time: the time will vary depending on the person with autism and the programme used. Most relationship-based interventions are lengthy and fairly labour-intensive, and may last for many years. For example, parents and children using the RDI programme usually undertake at least three hours a week of 'lab time', along with numerous teaching opportunities that happen during the day. Additional time is spent learning how to use the RDI programme (which may include training courses, travel and so on) (8).

Risks and safety

No risks are known for most relationship-based interventions, such as the RDI programme and the Son-Rise Program.

Specific forms of relationship-based intervention

Gentle teaching

Introduction

Gentle teaching is a non-violent approach for helping people with special needs and sometimes challenging behaviours.

The proponents believe that every human being needs to live connected with others in an equal and reciprocal relationship, and embedded in a loving and caring community. This community invites the individual to develop his qualities for the benefit of himself and the community.

It's essential that this relationship is unconditional, meaning that the person feels the carer's attitudes towards him or her don't depend on his or her behaviour (9).

Gentle teaching

Definition: a non-violent approach for helping people with special needs and sometimes challenging behaviours.

Aims: to teach the person to feel safe, engaged, loved and loving towards the care giver.

Who: people with special needs and sometimes challenging behaviours.

Evidence: insufficient research evidence to determine if gentle teaching has any benefits.

Risks: none.

Aims

Gentle teaching focuses on four primary goals of caregiving:

- teaching the person to feel safe with the care giver
- teaching the person to feel engaged with the care giver
- teaching the person to feel unconditionally loved by the care giver
- teaching the person to feel loving towards the care giver.

Gentle teaching started as a way of helping people with a learning disability and challenging behaviours. Over the years it has been used with other people, including people with mental health problems, people with Alzheimer's disease, and children with autism or ADHD.

Supporters of gentle teaching claim that the 'first and most important goal in gentle teaching is to develop companionship, the unconditional relationship which makes it possible to support the person in moments of stress. A side-effect may be that we can (hopefully) prevent harmful behaviours to occur. But this is not a goal in gentle teaching.' (9)

Evidence

Determining the benefits of gentle teaching for individuals on the autism spectrum is not currently possible. We must wait for further research of sufficiently high quality to be completed (3).

Risks and safety

No risks are known for gentle teaching.

Relationship development intervention (RDI)

Introduction

Relationship development intervention (RDI) is a parent-led approach based on the idea that children with autism have missed key developmental milestones (such as social referencing and joint attention) that enable them to think flexibly, regulate their emotions and understand social situations.

RDI seeks to give children another chance to master these milestones in the same way that they are mastered by typically developing children: through their relationship with their parents. An RDI consultant guides the parent, changing their communication and interaction style so that they can support their child to fill in the developmental gaps. This is done through everyday activities (such as washing up, cooking and going for a walk) some of which are videoed and shared with the family's consultant who then provides feedback on progress (8, 10).

> ## Relationship development intervention (RDI)
>
> **Definition:** a parent-led approach based on the idea that children with autism have missed key developmental milestones that enable them to think flexibly, regulate their emotions and understand social situations.
>
> **Aims:** to develop the ability to flexibly and creatively respond to novel situations.
>
> **Who:** mainly children, but could be people with autism of any age and any ability.
>
> **Evidence:** insufficient research evidence to determine if RDI has any benefits.
>
> **Risks:** none.

Aims

The aim of RDI is to help children to develop the ability to respond to increasingly challenging and unpredictable situations in flexible ways (4, 6).

RDI is aimed at children but is sometimes used for people with autism of any age and any ability.

Supporters of RDI claim that it can increase motivation to communicate and use meaningful reciprocal language, can reduce stereotyped behaviours and can improve flexible thinking, communication, creative information processing, problem-solving and self-development (8, 10).

Evidence

Determining the benefits of RDI for individuals on the autism spectrum is not currently possible. We must wait for further research of sufficiently high quality to be completed (4).

Risks and safety

No risks are known for RDI.

Son-Rise Program

Introduction

The Son-Rise Program (sometimes known as the Options Method) is based on the idea that children on the autism spectrum have trouble forming relationships with other people but can be helped to develop those relationships through playful interaction with an adult.

The adult follows the child's lead rather than imposing their own ideas of what the child should do. This includes 'joining' the child in their behaviour rather than trying to stop it. So, if the child is stacking blocks or flapping his hands, the adult does the same.

The aim is not simply to copy the activity but to build trust. By doing the same as the child, the adult shows the child that they are loved and accepted without judgement. It then becomes much easier to build a relationship. As the relationship develops the adult is able to use the child's own motivation to teach them new skills based around their own interests (11–12).

Aims

The Son-Rise Program aims to provide a comprehensive treatment programme for autism difficulties covering learning, development, communication, and skills acquisition.

Son-Rise Program

Definition: an intervention based on the idea that children with autism have trouble forming relationships with others.

Aims: to provide a comprehensive treatment programme for autism.

Who: children of any level of ability.

Evidence: insufficient research evidence to determine if the Son-Rise Program has any benefits.

Risks: none.

Choosing Autism Interventions: A Research-Based Guide © Research Autism and Autism West Midlands

The Son-Rise Program is used for children of all ages with any developmental difficulties.

The Autism Treatment Center of America has claimed that the Son-Rise Program can have a range of benefits, ranging from complete cure of children with autism to significant improvements in IQ, communication and social skills (11, 12).

Evidence

Determining the benefits of the Son-Rise Program for individuals on the autism spectrum is not currently possible. We must wait for further research of sufficiently high quality to be completed (5).

Risks and safety

No risks are associated with the Son-Rise Program.

Additional information

The Autism Treatment Center of America has been criticised on a number of occasions for the way it markets the Son-Rise Program, including being reprimanded by the Advertising Standards Authority in the UK (13, 14).

Further information

In this book: Please see How to use this book (page 11), Chapter 3 (page 38) for information about interventions, Chapter 4 (page 43) for information about how scientists evaluate those interventions, and Section 3 (page 284) for advice on making the decision about whether or not to use a specific intervention.

Websites: Please see www.researchautism.net/relationship-based-interventions for information about relationship-based interventions including information about specific interventions and details of scientific studies and trials.

References

1. American Psychiatric Association (2013) *Diagnostic and Statistical Manual of Mental Disorders – DSM-5*. Washington, D.C: American Psychiatric Association.

2. Research Autism (2014) *Relationship-based interventions and autism*. [online]. Available at: www.researchautism.net/relationship-based-interventions (accessed January 13, 2015).

3. Research Autism (2014) *Gentle teaching and autism* [online]. Available at: www.researchautism.net/gentle-teaching (accessed January 13, 2015).

4. Research Autism (2014) *Relationship Development Intervention and autism* [online]. Available at: www.researchautism.net/relationship-development-intervention-and-autism (accessed January 13, 2015).

5. Research Autism (2014) *Son-Rise program and autism* [online]. Available at: www.researchautism.net/son-rise-program-and-autism (accessed January 13, 2015).

6. National Institute for Health and Care Excellence (2013) *The Management and Support of Children and Young People on the Autism Spectrum*. London: National Institute for Health and Care Excellence.

7. Hofset T (undated) *Autism treatment is expensive* [online]. Available at: http://recoveringlucas.net/donate (accessed August 11, 2014). Please note: the page no longer exists.

8. Gutstein SE, Burgess AF & Montfort K (2007) Evaluation of the relationship development intervention program. *Autism: The International Journal of Research and Practice* **11** 397–411.

9. Gentle Teaching (2013) *Gentle teaching* [online]. Available at: www.gentleteaching.nl/gentle/index.php/en/wat-is-en/sum (accessed January 19, 2015).

10. Dynamic Connections Llc (2009) *What is relationship development intervention® program?* [online]. Available at: www.remediatingautism.com/dynamic-connections/services-for-familes/rdi/questions-and-answers.html (accessed January 19, 2015).

11. The Options Institute (2014) *Son-Rise*. Sheffield, MA: The Options Institute.

12. Kaufman RK (2005) Autism and the myth of false hope. *Autism Today*.

13. Association for Science in Autism Treatment (2010) *ASAT's Open Letter to Son-Rise Program's Raun Kaufman*. Hoboken, NJ: Association for Science in Autism Treatment.

14. Advertising Standards Authority (2010) *ASA Adjudication on The Option Institute and Fellowship*. London: Advertising Standards Authority.

Chapter 15:
Interventions for specific functions

Introduction

A number of autism interventions target specific functions, such as social communication, theory of mind or daily living skills.

These interventions can sometimes form part of a wider intervention programme or can be used alone. For example, comprehensive, multi-component behavioural and developmental interventions are usually designed to target a number of skills including social communication and social interaction.

Here we look at interventions which are specifically designed to target particular functions but which are not covered elsewhere in this book.

Evidence

High-quality evidence shows that people with autism have difficulties with some specific functions, such as the core issues of social communication and social interaction (1). Some high-quality evidence shows that some individuals on the autism spectrum have difficulties with other things, such as some thought processes and some skills used in everyday life (2).

Each functional intervention has its own evidence (or lack of evidence). For example, a very limited amount of evidence shows that social skills groups may help some adolescents on the autism spectrum. Determining the benefits of other interventions, such as functional-communication training or theory of mind training, for people on the autism spectrum is more difficult. We must wait for further research of sufficiently high quality to be completed (3–6).

NICE guidelines

The National Institute for Health and Care Excellence has provided some guidance on interventions for some specific functions. For example, it recommended the use of social skills groups or learning programmes for adults with social interaction difficulties. NICE also recommended the use of training programmes based on behavioural principles for adults who need help with daily living activities (6, 7).

Supply, quality and regulation

Functional interventions may be delivered by parents and carers, or professionals such as teachers and therapists.

Some regulating bodies for some providers of some interventions exist, such as for teachers, but no internationally recognised qualifications are available that are specific to the approaches we describe here.

Costs and time

Cost: the costs will depend largely on which intervention is used, who is providing the intervention, how long it takes to implement and the support materials purchased. For example, in the UK, various organisations advertise social skills group courses at a cost of £50–100 per participant.

Time: the length and frequency of the intervention depends on the intervention. For example, the length and frequency of a functional communication programme should be personalised to the needs of the individual on the autism spectrum, whereas most social skills groups are run for specific amounts of time over a set period, for instance, 90–120 minutes a week for 12 weeks (8).

Risks and safety

No risks are known for most interventions which target specific functions.

Specific forms of interventions for specific functions

Functional-communication training

Introduction

Functional-communication training is based on the idea that problem behaviours – such as self-harm, hitting other people or throwing tantrums – may be a form of communication. It requires a thorough assessment to identify the function ('or message') of each challenging behaviour, followed by instruction on how to communicate that message in a more acceptable form. For example, for a child who throws a tantrum as a way to get out of doing a difficult task, the instructor might teach the child to ask for a break by speaking, pointing or gesturing when a task becomes challenging (8).

> **Functional-communication training**
>
> **Definition:** an intervention based on the idea that problem behaviours may be a form of communication.
>
> **Aims:** to teach people with autism to use functional forms of communication instead of problem behaviours.
>
> **Who:** people with autism of all ages and ability.
>
> **Evidence:** weak evidence suggests there may be some benefits.
>
> **Risks:** none.

Aims

The aim of functional-communication training is to teach people with autism to use functional forms of communication as opposed to problem behaviours as a form of communication (8, 9).

Functional-communication training is used for people of any age and level of ability who are having difficulty communicating a need (and therefore show challenging behaviour).

The supporters of functional-communication training claim that it can reduce challenging behaviours and improve quality of life.

Evidence

Functional communication training may provide some benefits for individuals on the autism spectrum but the quality of the evidence is weak. Further research of better quality is required before we can be sure (3).

Risks

No risks are associated with functional-communication training.

Social skills groups

Introduction

Social skills groups provide an opportunity for individuals on the autism spectrum to practice and improve their social skills in a safe, supportive and structured environment. They meet on a regular basis and usually a professional runs the meeting. Some groups consist only of autistic people, although some may also include non-autistic people who demonstrate appropriate social skills. A social skills session typically includes a structured lesson on a specific skill, demonstration of the skill, role playing with practice of the skill, discussion, and individualised performance feedback (10).

Social skills groups

Definition: groups of people with autism which meet to practice and improve their social skills.

Aims: to improve the social skills of people with autism.

Who: people with autism of all ages that are higher-functioning.

Evidence: very limited amount of research evidence that social skills groups may provide some benefits.

Risks: none.

Aims

The aim of social skills groups is to help people with autism to improve their social skills.

Social skills groups tend to be aimed at people with autism of all ages who are higher-functioning.

Some people claim that social skills groups can improve a range of social interactions (10).

Evidence

Social skills groups can help people with autism become more aware of social cues and understand how to interact with others according to a very limited amount of research evidence of sufficiently high quality (4).

Risks

No risks are known for social skills groups.

Theory of mind training

Introduction

Theory of mind training programmes are designed to teach individuals with autism how to recognise mental states (thoughts, beliefs, desires, intentions and emotions) in themselves or others, and then be able to make sense of and predict actions. A variety of programmes teach theory of mind. For example, some programmes are based on teaching children to visualise other people's thoughts and emotions by imagining those thoughts and emotions as pictures or thought bubbles (11).

Theory of mind training

Definition: teaching individuals to recognise their own mental states and those of others.

Aims: to help people to improve social behaviour and become more empathetic.

Who: people with autism of all ages that are higher-functioning.

Evidence: insufficient evidence to determine if theory of mind training has any benefits.

Risks: none.

Aims

Theory of mind training is designed to help people with autism who are higher-functioning.

The aim is to help people to recognise their own mental states and those of others.

Some people claim that it can help people with autism to become more empathetic and improve social behaviour (12).

Evidence

Determining the benefits of theory of mind training for individuals on the autism spectrum is not currently possible. We must wait for further research of sufficiently high quality to be completed (5).

Risks

No risks are known for theory of mind training.

Further information

In this book: Please see How to use this book (page 11), Chapter 3 (page 38) for information about interventions, Chapter 4 (page 43) for information about how scientists evaluate those interventions, and Section 3 (page 284) for advice on making the decision about whether or not to use a specific intervention.

Websites: Please see www.researchautism.net/specific-function-interventions for information about interventions for specific functions including information about specific interventions and details of scientific studies and trials.

References

1. American Psychiatric Association (2013) *Diagnostic and Statistical Manual of Mental Disorders – DSM-5*. Washington, D.C: American Psychiatric Association.

2. Fletcher-Watson S, McConnell F, Manola E & McConachie H (2014) Interventions based on the Theory of Mind cognitive model for autism spectrum disorder (ASD). *Cochrane Database of Systematic Reviews* **3** CD008785.

3. Research Autism (2014) *Functional communication and autism* [online]. Available at: www.researchautism.net/functional-communication-training (accessed January 13, 2015).

4. Research Autism (2014) *Social skills groups and autism* [online]. Available at: www.researchautism.net/social-skills-groups-and-autism (accessed January 13, 2015).

5. Research Autism (2014) *Theory of mind training and autism* [online]. Available at: www.researchautism.net/theory-of-mind-training-and-autism (accessed January 13, 2015).

6. National Institute for Health and Care Excellence (2012) *Autism: Recognition, referral, diagnosis and management of adults on the autism spectrum*. London: National Institute for Health and Care Excellence.

7. National Institute for Health and Care Excellence (2013) *The Management and Support of Children and Young People on the Autism Spectrum*. London: National Institute for Health and Care Excellence.

8. Mancil G (2006) Functional communication training: a review of the literature related to children with autism. *Education and Training in Developmental Disabilities* **41** 213–224.

9. Kurtz PF, Boelter EW, Jarmolowicz DP, Chin MD & Hagopian LP (2011) An analysis of functional communication training as an empirically supported treatment for problem behavior displayed by individuals with intellectual disabilities. *Research in Developmental Disabilities* **32** 2935–42.

10. Williams White S, Keonig K & Scahill L (2007) Social skills development in children with autism spectrum disorders: a review of the intervention research. *Journal of Autism and Developmental Disorders* **37** 1858–68.

11. IAN Network (2007) *Cognitive Theories Explaining ASDs*. Baltimore, MD: IAN Network.

12. Begeer S, Gevers C, Clifford P, Verhoeve M, Kat K, Hoddenbach E & Boer F (2011) Theory of Mind training in children with autism: a randomized controlled trial. *Journal of Autism and Developmental Disorders* **41** 997–1006.

Chapter 16:
Technology-based behavioural interventions

Introduction

A number of technology-based behavioural interventions do not fall into any of the other categories in this book.

Here we focus on those interventions which use (mostly) low-tech, visual support tools such as pictures and photographs. For example, social stories are designed to help individuals on the autism spectrum to understand specific social situations and teach them what is appropriate to do. Visual schedules provide individuals on the autism spectrum with a way to predict and understand upcoming events (1, 2).

Evidence

High-quality evidence shows that people with autism have difficulties in social communication, social interaction and restricted and repetitive patterns of behaviour. Also, high-quality evidence shows that some children with autism have difficulty reaching certain developmental milestones associated with the development of social communication skills and social interaction (3, 4).

Determining the benefits of the interventions in this chapter for people on the autism spectrum is difficult. We must wait for further research of sufficiently high quality to be completed (5, 6, 7).

NICE guidelines

The National Institute for Health and Care Excellence has not made specific recommendations on the use of most of these other behavioural and developmental interventions.

Supply, quality and regulation

Most of these interventions can be implemented by a variety of people, including parents and carers, as well as professionals such as teachers. No internationally recognised qualification for the delivery of these interventions exists, but we recommend that people seek advice from a professional when first setting up the intervention.

Costs and time

Cost: the costs will depend on the intervention, who is implementing the intervention, how long it takes to implement, any training undertaken and any support materials bought. For example, for video modelling you may need to buy a computer and a camcorder, and software to transfer the videos from the camcorder to the computer.

Time: the length and frequency of the intervention will depend on the needs of the individual. For example, some individuals with autism may need to be shown the same social story on several occasions, sometimes more than a dozen, on a daily or weekly basis, to have the desired effect.

Risks and safety

No risks are known for any of the interventions we describe here.

Specific forms of technology-based behavioural interventions

Social stories

Introduction

Social stories are for teaching social skills to individuals on the autism spectrum. They provide an individual with explanations about situations that they may find difficult or confusing.

Some are written on single sheets of paper, others are written in booklets and some are recorded onto tape or video. The author of the story may read it to the individual with autism, record it so that it can be played back as required, or the individual may read it for themselves (1, 8).

Aims

Social stories were first developed for use with children with autism, but have also been used with adolescents and adults with a range of conditions.

Social stories

Definition: stories which provide explanations of specific social situations.

Aims: to increase understanding of, and comfort in, specific social situations.

Who: people with autism of any age who have the ability to understand stories.

Evidence: weak evidence suggests there may be some benefits.

Risks: none.

The primary purpose of social stories is to increase an individual's understanding of specific social situations, to make the person more comfortable in those situations, and possibly to suggest appropriate responses when in those situations (1).

Some people claim that social stories can teach children specific social skills, teach children how to make choices, increase desired behaviours (such as length and frequency of social interactions), decrease undesired behaviours, and improve the psychological well-being of the child (1, 8).

Evidence

Social stories may provide some benefits for individuals on the autism spectrum but the quality of the evidence is weak. Further research of better quality is required before we can be sure (5).

Risks

No risks are known for social stories.

Video modelling

Introduction

Video modelling is a method of teaching an individual a behaviour or a skill by watching a video of someone (the model) demonstrating that behaviour or skill. The model can be someone else (such as a parent or sibling) or it can be the individual themselves, when the process is called video self-modelling (VSM). Video modelling is sometimes used alongside or as part of other interventions, such as social stories or visual schedules (9, 10).

Video modelling

Definition: learning a skill by watching a video of someone demonstrating that skill.

Aims: to teach an individual to change their behaviour and learn new skills.

Who: people with autism of any age who have the ability to watch videos and who have developed imitation skills.

Evidence: weak evidence suggests there may be some benefits.

Risks: none.

Aims

Video modelling is for people with autism of any age who are able to watch videos and who have developed imitation skills.

The main aim of video modelling is to teach an individual to change their behaviour and learn new skills. For example, it may be used to teach a child with autism how to use the toilet by themselves or how to engage in conversation.

The supporters of video modelling claim that it can teach a wide variety of social and everyday skills, such as how to interact with other people or how to buy things. They also claim that video modelling can teach an individual how to apply previously learnt behaviours and skills in new settings (9, 10).

Evidence

Video modelling may provide some benefits for individuals on the autism spectrum but the quality of the evidence is weak. Further research of better quality is required before we can be sure (6).

Risks

No risks are known for video modelling.

Visual schedules

Introduction

A visual schedule is a set of pictures that communicates a series of activities or the steps of a specific activity. It shows an individual with autism what activities will occur, and in what sequence. A schedule can be created using photographs, pictures, written words, physical objects or any combination of these items. Schedules can be put into notebooks, onto a wall or schedule board or onto a computer. Most visual schedules are introduced with adult guidance that gradually decreases with time. Eventually, the individual with autism may learn to create their own schedules (2, 11).

Visual schedules

Definition: a set of pictures that communicates a series of activities or the steps of a specific activity.

Aims: to provide a way to predict or understand upcoming events to increase independence or reduce problem behaviours.

Who: people with autism of any age who can understand visual information.

Evidence: weak evidence suggests there may be some benefits.

Risks: none.

Aims

Visual schedules are for people with autism of any age who have the ability to understand visual information.

The main purpose of visual schedules is to give the individual a way to predict or understand upcoming events in order to reduce anxiety and problem behaviours and increase independence.

Some people claim that visual schedules can increase desired behaviour and self-management, enhance the ability to anticipate and accept transitions, improve communication and everyday skills, and decrease disruptive behaviour (2, 11).

Evidence

Visual schedules may provide some benefits for individuals on the autism spectrum but the quality of the evidence is weak. Further research of better quality is required before we can be sure (7).

Risks

No risks are known for visual schedules.

Further information

In this book: Please see How to use this book (page 11), Chapter 3 (page 38) for information about interventions, Chapter 4 (page 43) for information about how scientists evaluate those interventions, and Section 3 (page 284) for advice on making the decision about whether or not to use a specific intervention.

Websites: Please see www.researchautism.net/technology-based-behvioural-interventions for information about other behavioural and developmental interventions including information about specific interventions and details of scientific studies and trials.

References

1. Gray CA & Garand JD (1993) Social stories: improving responses of students with autism with accurate social information. *Focus on Autism and Other Developmental Disabilities* **8** 1–10.

2. Kamp L & McErlean T (2000) *Visual Schedule Systems*. Vancouver, BC: SET-BC Learning Centre.

3. National Institute for Health and Care Excellence (2012) *Autism: Recognition, referral, diagnosis and management of adults on the autism spectrum*. London: National Institute for Health and Care Excellence.

4 National Institute for Health and Care Excellence (2013) *The Management and Support of Children and Young People on the Autism Spectrum*. London: National Institute for Health and Care Excellence.

5. Research Autism (2014) *Social stories and autism* [online]. Available at: www.researchautism.net/social-stories-and-autism (accessed January 13, 2015).

6. Research Autism (2014) *Video modelling and autism* [online]. Available at: www.researchautism.net/video-modelling-and-autism (accessed January 13, 2015).

7. Research Autism (2014) *Visual schedules and autism* [online]. Available at: www.researchautism.net/visual-schedules-and-autism (accessed January 13, 2015).

8. Test DW, Richter S, Knight V & Spooner F (2010) A comprehensive review and meta-analysis of the social sories literature. *Focus on Autism and Other Developmental Disabilities* **26** 49–62.

9. Banda DR, Matuszny R & Turkan S (2007) Video modeling strategies to enhance appropriate behaviors in children with autism spectrum disorders. *Teaching Exceptional Children* July/August 47–52.

10. Wang H-T & Koyama T (2014) An analysis and review of the literature and a three-tier video modeling intervention model. *Research in Autism Spectrum Disorders* **8** 746–758.

11. Knight V, Sartini E & Spriggs AD (2014) Evaluating visual activity schedules as evidence-based practice for individuals with autism spectrum disorders. *Journal of Autism and Developmental Disorders* **45** (1) 157–178

Chapter 17:
Medications

Introduction

Medications (also known as pharmaceutical drugs, medicines, or medicaments) are chemical substances intended for use in the medical diagnosis, cure, treatment, or prevention of disease (1, 2).

Many different kinds of medication are used to treat people on the autism spectrum. These include but are not limited to: anticonvulsants, antidepressants, antipsychotics, anxiolytics, hormones, immunoglobulins, stimulant medications and many others. None of these medications was initially designed specifically to treat autism, but instead target other conditions such as high blood pressure, epilepsy, ADHD and drug dependency (3, 4).

Most of these medications are psychotropic, that is, they are designed to target the brain and are believed to work by changing the amount or action of neurotransmitters – naturally occurring chemicals found in the brain. Other drugs target other systems including the hormone system, the gastrointestinal system, and the immune system (3, 4).

Medications are available in many forms including tablets, capsules, liquids, infusions and injections. The same medication may have several different brand names. For example, the antipsychotic haloperidol is marketed as Dozic®, Haldol®, and Serenace® (5).

Evidence

Most medications have no effect on the core features of autism according to a limited amount of high-quality research evidence.

Some medications (such as some of the newer, atypical antipsychotics like risperidone) may be effective in treating some of the challenging behaviours shown by some people on the autism spectrum according to a limited amount of high quality research evidence (6).

Choosing Autism Interventions: A Research-Based Guide © Research Autism and Autism West Midlands

Methylphenidate may be beneficial for the treatment of hyperactivity, impulsivity and inattention in some children and young people on the autism spectrum according to a very limited amount of research evidence of sufficiently high quality (7).

Melatonin may be effective in reducing some sleep disturbances in some people on the autism spectrum according to a very limited amount of research evidence of sufficiently high quality (8).

Secretin provides no benefits to people on the autism spectrum according to a limited amount of research evidence of sufficiently high quality (9).

Very little high-quality research evidence supports the effectiveness of most other medications for treating the other issues facing people on the autism spectrum (10, 11).

NICE guidelines

The National Institute for Health and Care Excellence has recommended that (10, 11):

- no medications should be used to treat the core features of autism
- some medications may be used to treat co-existing problems, such as attention deficit hyperactivity disorder, but only as part of an overall treatment programme that follows existing NICE guidance for those co-existing problems
- some antipsychotics may be used for challenging behaviour but only when psychosocial or other interventions could not be delivered because of the severity of the challenging behaviour, and then only under very strictly controlled conditions
- some medications (such as secretin) should never be used.

Supply, quality and regulation

Some medications are very powerful, with many potential side effects and contraindications (specific situations where the medication may be harmful, such as if the person is taking other medication, or if the person has other conditions). For this reason they should only be obtained on prescription from a paediatrician or psychiatrist.

In the UK, medications and medical devices are regulated by the Medicines and Healthcare Products Regulatory Agency. They authorise medicines before they can be marketed, taking both their safety and effectiveness into account (2).

Costs and time

The cost of different medications depends on a number of different factors including: the type of drug, whether it is a new drug or an old one, whether it is a generic drug or one with a brand name, where it is sold and the supplier.

In the UK most medications are available at reduced rates or free of charge to patients on the NHS. In other countries the costs may be covered by some insurance policies.

The time required to use different medications depends on a number of factors. For example, some medications need to be taken once or twice a day but do not require direct supervision. Other medications (such as depot injections) only need to be given once every few weeks or months but they need to be given by an experienced clinical practitioner (which may require the recipient to travel to the clinic). All medications require careful monitoring and follow up.

Risks and safety

Many medications contain active ingredients that can have strong effects on the mind and the body. For example, antipsychotics can cause side effects such as movement disorders, dry mouth, blurred vision, constipation, dizziness or light-headedness, and weight gain. More rarely, antipsychotics may cause more serious side effects such as changes to blood sugar levels or blood lipid levels, neuroleptic malignant syndrome (fever, faster breathing, sweating, muscle stiffness and reduced consciousness), and cardiac arrhythmia (irregular heart beat) (12).

Some substances can interact with some medications in ways that can cause problems. For example, vitamin B-6 can reduce the effectiveness of some anticonvulsants, such as sodium valproate, carbamazepine and phenytoin (13).

Some medications may be unsuitable for certain groups of people. For example, the mental health charity Mind recommends you should use antipsychotics with caution if you have other medical conditions, such as liver or kidney disease, cardiovascular (heart and circulation) disease, or a family history of diabetes (14).

Specific forms of medication

Alpha 2-adrenergic receptor agonists

Introduction

Alpha 2-adrenergic receptor agonists (also called antihypertensives) are drugs used to treat a range of conditions, including high blood pressure.

Specific alpha 2-adrenergic receptor agonists include clonidine (Catapres®) and guanfacine (Tenex®).

Alpha 2-adrenergic receptor agonists work by decreasing the heart rate and relaxing the blood vessels so that blood can flow more easily through the body. They also regulate the amount and action of noradrenaline (a neurotransmitter and hormone, also called norepinephrine, particularly in the US) (15).

> **Alpha 2-adrenergic receptor agonists**
>
> **Definition:** drugs used to treat a range of conditions including high blood pressure.
>
> **Aims:** to reduce impulsivity, inattention, and hyperactivity by regulating noradrenaline.
>
> **Who:** people with autism of all ages and all levels of ability.
>
> **Evidence:** insufficient evidence to determine if antihypertensives have any benefits.
>
> **Risks:** minor side effects, such as dry mouth, tiredness, weakness.

Aims

Some alpha 2-adrenergic receptor agonists have been shown to be effective in reducing impulsivity, inattention, and hyperactivity associated with attention deficit hyperactivity disorder.

Because of this some people think they could also be used to treat these behaviours in people on the autism spectrum (16, 17).

Evidence

Determining the benefits of alpha 2-adrenergic receptor agonists for individuals on the autism spectrum is not currently possible. We must wait for further research of sufficiently high quality to be completed (18).

Risks

Different alpha 2-adrenergic receptors may produce different side effects. For example, clonidine may produce a number of side effects in some people including dry mouth, tiredness, and weakness (15).

Anticonvulsants

Introduction

Anticonvulsants (also known as antiepileptics) are a group of drugs which aim to prevent or reduce the severity of fits (convulsions) in various types of epilepsy.

Some anticonvulsants are also used to treat other conditions. For example, some forms of sodium valproate are used to treat the symptoms of bipolar disorder – such as mania, impulsivity, irritability and aggression.

There are a number of different anticonvulsants including lamotrigine

Anticonvulsants

Definition: drugs which prevent or reduce the severity of fits in various types of epilepsy.

Aims: as well as managing epilepsy, some believe they can improve behaviours by regulating serotonin.

Who: people with autism of all ages and all levels of ability, especially those with abnormal EEG activity.

Evidence: insufficient evidence to determine if anticonvulsants have any benefits.

Risks: some significant risks with some anticonvulsants, such as liver failure.

(Lamictal®), levetiracetam (Keppra®), sodium valproate (Depakote®) and topiramate (Topamax®).

Anticonvulsants appear to work by regulating the amount of key neurotransmitters in the brain (especially serotonin) which reduces the amount and severity of fits (19).

Aims

Many people with autism also have epilepsy (20), so they may be prescribed anticonvulsants to manage their epilepsy.

Some people think that anticonvulsants could be used to reduce some of the core symptoms of autism (such as social and communication difficulties and repetitive, compulsive behaviour) (21).

Evidence

Some anticonvulsants (such as sodium valproate) have been studied more than others (such as topiramate). However, determining the benefits of anticonvulsants for individuals on the autism spectrum is not currently possible. We must wait for further research of sufficiently high quality to be completed (22).

Risks

Different anticonvulsants carry different risks. For example, according to the American Society of Health-System Pharmacists, 'Valproic acid [sodium valproate] may cause serious or life-threatening damage to the liver and is most likely to occur within the first six months of therapy. The risk of developing liver damage is greater in children who are younger than two years of age and are also taking more than one medication to prevent seizures, have certain inherited diseases that may prevent the body from changing food to energy normally, or any condition that affects the ability to think, learn, and understand.' (23)

Additional information

Anticonvulsants should not be used for the management of the core features of autism in children, young people and adults according to the National Institute for Health and Care Excellence (10, 11).

Antidepressants

Introduction

Antidepressants are drugs used to treat people with mental health problems such as depression and anxiety.

Numerous different types of antidepressants have been developed, including:

- SSRIs (selective serotonin reuptake inhibitors) including citalopram (Celexa®), fluoxetine (Prozac ®), fluvoxamine (Faverin®) and sertraline (Lustral®)
- SNRIs (serotonin and noradrenaline reuptake inhibitors) including venlafaxine (Effexor®)
- NASSAs (noradrenaline and specific serotoninergic antidepressants) including mirtazapine (Avanza®)
- Tricyclics including imipramine (Tofranil®) and nortriptyline (Allegron®)
- MAOIs (monoamine oxidase inhibitors) including phenelzine (Nardil®) and selegiline (Eldepryl®).

In practice, the newest types of antidepressants (such as SSRIs, SNRIs and NASSAs) are more likely to be prescribed than the older types of antidepressants (such as tricyclics and MAOIs).

Antidepressants

Definition: drugs used to treat people with depression, anxiety or other mental health problems.

Aims: to treat mental health problems and challenging behaviour by regulating serotonin and dopamine.

Who: adolescents and adults with autism of all levels of ability.

Evidence: insufficient evidence to determine if antidepressants have any benefits.

Risks: some significant risks, such as a danger of suicide.

The exact mechanism of antidepressants is unknown but it is assumed they work by changing the level and action of one or more neurotransmitters in the brain (such as serotonin and dopamine) (24, 25).

Aims

Some people think that antidepressants can be used treat people on the autism spectrum who have mental health problems, such as anger, irritability and aggression, or challenging behaviours such as self-injurious behaviour, inattention and hyperactivity.

Some people think that they can also be used to treat the core features of autism (such as poor social communication and poor social interaction, and restricted and repetitive behaviours) (26).

Evidence

Determining the benefits of antidepressants for individuals on the autism spectrum is not currently possible. We must wait for further research of sufficiently high quality to be completed. But a limited amount of evidence shows that they may be harmful to some individuals. For example, according to a Cochrane Review carried out in 2013:

'There is no evidence that selective serotonin reuptake inhibitors (SSRIs) are effective as a treatment for children with autism. In fact, there is emerging evidence that they are not effective and can cause harm.

'For adults, small positive effects have been seen with fewer side effects reported with fluoxetine and fluvoxamine, but the possible risk of bias and small sample size of the trials mean there is not strong evidence to support these treatments.' (26, 27)

Risks

Some antidepressants carry quite significant and serious risks. For example, according to the American Society of Health-System Pharmacists:

'A small number of children, teenagers, and young adults (up to 24 years of age) who took antidepressants ('mood elevators') such as citalopram during clinical studies became suicidal (thinking about harming or killing oneself or planning or trying to do so).' (28)

The most common side effects include drowsiness, blurred vision, nausea and vomiting. However, this usually settles down as an individual gets used to the drug. The Cochrane review looking at SSRIs also reported that 'with monitoring, dose adjustment and time, [most] adverse effects [can be] resolved' (26).

Additional information

Antidepressant medication should not be used for the routine management of core symptoms of autism in children, young people and adults according to the National Institute for Health and Care Excellence (10, 11).

Antipsychotics

Introduction

Antipsychotics (also known as neuroleptics or major tranquillisers) are a type of drug used to treat a range of mental health problems including psychosis, anxiety and dementia.

Antipsychotics come in two main types:

- The older, typical or conventional antipsychotics, which include haloperidol, chlorpromazine, fluphenazine, molindone, piperidinephenthiazine, trifluoperazine, thiothixene, and trifluperidol.

Antipsychotics

Definition: drugs used to treat a range of mental health problems including psychosis, anxiety and dementia.

Aims: to treat challenging behaviour by regulating the action of various neurotransmitters.

Who: adolescents and adults with both autism and challenging behaviours.

Evidence: limited amount of research evidence that some atypical antipsychotics, such as risperidone, may provide some benefits.

Risks: some significant risks, such as weight gain.

Choosing Autism Interventions: A Research-Based Guide © Research Autism and Autism West Midlands

- The newer, atypical antipsychotics which include aripiprazole (Abilify®), clozapine (Clozaril®), olanzapine (Zolafren®), pimozide (Orap®), quetiapine (Seroquel®), and risperidone (Risperdal®).

Antipsychotics work by changing the amounts and the effects of different neurotransmitters (chemicals in the brain). Traditional antipsychotics work mainly by reducing the amount and the action of dopamine. Most atypical antipsychotics work by changing the amount and the action of a range of neurotransmitters including dopamine, serotonin, noradrenaline and acetylcholine (12, 29).

Aims

Some people think that antipsychotics can be used to treat some of the more challenging problems faced by individuals on the autism spectrum. For example, according to Posey:

'Atypical antipsychotics have become indispensable in the treatment of a variety of symptoms in autism. They are frequently used to treat irritability and associated behaviours including aggression and self-injury. They may also be efficacious for hyperactivity and stereotyped behaviour.' (30)

Evidence

Some of the newer, atypical antipsychotics, like risperidone, affect challenging behaviours and may provide some benefits for some individuals on the autism spectrum, according to a limited amount of research evidence of sufficiently high quality (10, 11, 31).

Risks

According to the Medicines and Healthcare Products Regulatory Agency:

'As with all medicines, antipsychotics can produce side effects in some people. The most common include movement disorders (referred to as extrapyramidal side effects) such as akathisia (an unpleasant feeling of restlessness with involuntary body movements) or dystonia (abnormal muscle contractions); dry mouth, blurred vision and constipation (often called 'anticholinergic effects' because they result from blockade of cholinergic receptors); dizziness or light headedness; and weight gain.

'Rarely, antipsychotics may cause more serious side effects such as changes to blood sugar levels or blood lipid levels, neuroleptic malignant syndrome (fever, faster breathing, sweating, muscle stiffness and reduced consciousness), and cardiac arrhythmias (irregular heart beat)' (12).

Additional information

Antipsychotic medication is not recommended for the management of the core symptoms of autism in adults nor in children or young people, according to the National Institute for Health and Care Excellence.

However, it does recommend that antipsychotic medication should be considered for managing challenging behaviour when psychosocial (see page 228) or other interventions are insufficient or could not be delivered because of the severity of the behaviour.

It recommends that antipsychotic medication should be initially prescribed and monitored by a paediatrician or psychiatrist who should identify the target behaviour, review effectiveness and stop the treatment if there is no response (10, 11).

Anxiolytics and hypnotics

Introduction

Anxiolytics (also known as anti-anxiety agents or minor tranquillisers) are drugs used to treat feelings of anxiety or nervousness. Hynoptics (also known as sleeping pills or sedatives) are drugs used to treat sleeplessness.

Benzodiazepines are the most commonly used anxiolytics and hypnotics as they have fewer side effects than other anxiolytics and hypnotics such as barbiturates. Benzodiazepines include diazepam (Valium®), buspirone (BuSpar®) and lorazepam (Ativan®).

Choosing Autism Interventions: A Research-Based Guide © Research Autism and Autism West Midlands

Benzodiazepines are believed to work by modifying the amount and action of gamma-aminobutyric acid (GABA) (32, 33).

Aims

Some people think that anxiolytics and hypnotics can be used treat people on the autism spectrum who suffer from anxiety, nervousness, sleeplessness or other problems (34).

Evidence

Determining the benefits of anxiolytics and hypnotics for individuals on the autism spectrum is not currently possible. We must wait for further research of sufficiently high quality to be completed (35).

Anxiolytics and hypnotics

Definition: drugs used to treat people with anxiety, nervousness or sleeplessness.

Aims: to treat anxiety and other problems by regulating the amount and action of gamma-aminobutyric acid.

Who: adolescents and adults with autism of all levels of ability.

Evidence: insufficient evidence to determine if anxiolytics and hypnotics have any benefits.

Risks: vary, including withdrawal problems.

Risks

According to the British National Formulary, older anxiolytics 'such as meprobamate and barbiturates are not recommended – they have more side effects and interactions than benzodiazepines and are much more dangerous in overdosage.' (32).

Individual barbiturates also carry quite significant and serious risks. For example, diazepam can cause a variety of side effects including drowsiness, light-headedness and confusion (36).

In addition, withdrawal of any kind of anxiolytic can also carry significant and serious risks. For example, according to the British National Formulary (33):

'Withdrawal of a benzodiazepine should be gradual because abrupt withdrawal may produce confusion, toxic psychosis, convulsions, or a condition resembling delirium tremens. Abrupt withdrawal of a barbiturate is even more likely to have serious effects.'

Additional information

The British National Formulary reported:

'Benzodiazepines are indicated for the short-term relief (two to four weeks only) of anxiety that is severe, disabling, or causing the patient unacceptable distress, occurring alone or in association with insomnia or short-term psychosomatic, organic, or psychotic illness.

'The use of benzodiazepines to treat short-term 'mild' anxiety is inappropriate.

'Benzodiazepines should be used to treat insomnia only when it is severe, disabling, or causing the patient extreme distress.' (33)

Beta-blockers

Introduction

Beta-blockers are drugs which are used to treat a range of conditions including hypertension, angina, irregular heartbeat, heart failure and heart attack.

Beta-blockers include acebutolol (Sectral®), atenolol (Tenormin®), celiprolol (Celectol®), nadolol (Corgard®), oxprenolol, pindolol (Visken®), propranolol (Syprol®) and sotalol (Sotacor®).

Beta-bockers appear to work by blocking the beta-adrenoceptors (parts of a cell membrane) in the heart, blood vessels, bronchi, pancreas, and liver (37).

> ## Beta-blockers
>
> **Definition:** drugs used to treat people with hypertension, angina, irregular heartbeat.
>
> **Aims:** to reduce challenging behaviours and to improve communication and cognitive skills by blocking beta-adrenoceptors.
>
> **Who:** a range of people on the autism spectrum.
>
> **Evidence:** insufficient evidence to determine if beta-blockers have any benefits.
>
> **Risks:** various including life-threatening heart failure.

Aims

Some people think that beta-blockers can be used treat people with learning disabilities, including some people on the autism spectrum, who have challenging behaviour. Some people think that specific beta-blockers, such as propranolol, can be used to increase and improve communication skills, such as word fluency (38).

Evidence

Determining the benefits of beta-blockers for individuals on the autism spectrum is not currently possible. We must wait for further research of sufficiently high quality to be completed (39).

Risks

According to the British National Formulary: 'Beta-blockers slow the heart and can depress the myocardium; they are contraindicated in patients with second- or third-degree heart block. Beta-blockers should also be avoided in patients with worsening unstable heart failure; care is required when initiating a beta-blocker in those with stable heart failure. Sotalol may prolong the QT interval, and it occasionally causes life-threatening ventricular arrhythmias.' (40)

Cholinesterase inhibitors

Introduction

Cholinesterase inhibitors are drugs which are used to slow the mental decline or stabilise the symptoms of conditions such as Alzheimer's disease.

There are a number of different cholinesterase inhibitors including donepezil (Aricept®), galantamine (Reminyl®), rivastigmine (Exelon®) and tacrine (Cognex®).

Cholinesterase inhibitors appear to work by inhibiting (reducing the effect) of cholinesterase, a chemical found in the brain.

This appears to improve cognitive functioning in a number of areas, such as memory and the ability to pay attention (41).

Aims

Some people think that cholinesterase inhibitors may help some individuals on the autism spectrum by decreasing their restricted and repetitive patterns of thinking, and by improving their ability to pay attention, to process emotions and to interact with other people (42).

Evidence

Determining the benefits of cholinesterase inhibitors for individuals on the autism spectrum is not currently possible. We must wait for further research of sufficiently high quality to be completed (43).

Cholinesterase inhibitors

Definition: drugs used to slow down or stabilise the symptoms of conditions such as Alzheimer's disease.

Aims: in autism, to improve cognitive skills by regulating cholinesterase.

Who: people with autism of all ages and all levels of ability.

Evidence: insufficient evidence to determine if cholinesterase inhibitors have any benefits.

Risks: some minor risks eg. nausea.

Risks

Different cholinesterase inhibitors carry different risks. For example, according to the American Society of Health-System Pharmacists, donepezil can cause a wide range of side effects including nausea, vomiting and diarrhoea (44).

Additional information

The National Institute for Health and Care Excellence recommended: 'Do not use drugs specifically designed to improve cognitive functioning (for example, cholinesterase inhibitors) for the management of core symptoms of autism or routinely for associated cognitive or behavioural problems in adults.' (10, 11)

Hormones

Introduction

Hormones are the body's chemical messengers. They travel in the bloodstream to tissues or organs. They work slowly and affect many different processes, including growth and development, metabolism, sexual function and mood (45).

Many different hormones have been suggested as interventions for people on the autism spectrum.

Melatonin is released in the evening, makes us drowsy and prepares our body for sleep. It helps to set our body clock (circadian rhythms) (46).

Oxytocin appears to play a key role in social behaviour and social understanding. For example, it helps to regulate sexual behaviour, strengthens bonds between mothers and infants, strengthens bonds between adults, and appears to cause paranoia when combined with the stress hormone cortisol. It is also involved in social memory and recognition (47).

Secretin helps promote the digestion of food. It stimulates the stomach to produce the enzyme pepsin, the liver to produce bile, and the pancreas to produce digestive juices that help neutralise acidity in the intestines (48).

Aims

Some people think that melatonin can help people with autism who are experiencing severe sleep disturbances. For example, they think it can make them go to sleep more quickly, increase the total sleep time, and improve the quality of sleep (46).

Hormones

Definition: the body's chemical messengers, affecting growth, metabolism, sexual function and mood.

Aims: various, including to reduce sleep problems, improve sociability, reduce the core features of autism.

Who: varies depending on the hormone.

Evidence: very limited research evidence for melatonin, insufficient research evidence for oxytocin, limited evidence against secretin.

Risks: vary from hormone to hormone.

Some people think that oxytocin can reduce repetitive behaviours, and to improve some aspects of social information processing, in some individuals with autism (47).

Some people think that giving secretin to people on the autism spectrum will aid digestion. This is supposed to ease any gastrointestinal problems and bring about improvements in other areas, such as communication (48).

Evidence

Melatonin may provide some benefits for some individuals on the autism spectrum according to a very limited amount of research evidence of sufficiently high quality (7).

Determining the benefits of oxytocin for individuals on the autism spectrum is not currently possible. We must wait for further research of sufficiently high quality to be completed (49).

Secretin does not provide any benefits for individuals on the autism spectrum according to a limited amount of research evidence of sufficiently high quality (9).

Risks

Hormones are powerful chemicals and different hormones may produce different side effects.

Melatonin is generally regarded as safe in recommended doses for short-term use. However, some concerns have been raised about the risks of blood clotting abnormalities, increased risk of seizure, and disorientation if you overdose (50).

Side effects with oxytocin are not common but may include: allergic reactions, difficulty urinating, chest pain or irregular heartbeat, difficulty breathing, confusion, sudden weight gain or excessive swelling, severe headache, rash, excessive vaginal bleeding, seizures (51).

Common side effects of secretin include flushing of the face, neck, and chest immediately after a dose. Less common side effects are vomiting, diarrhoea, fainting, blood clot, fever, and rapid heartbeat. Some people can have allergic reactions including hives, redness of the skin, and a life-threatening allergic reaction (anaphylaxis) (52).

Additional information

The guidance from the National Institute for Health and Care Excellence varies, depending on the specific hormone. For example, it advises:

'Do not use oxytocin for the management of core symptoms of autism in adults' and 'Do not use secretin for the management of core symptoms of autism in adults.' (11)

However, it advises that melatonin may be appropriate to aid sleep but that it should:

- only be used following consultation with a specialist paediatrician or psychiatrist with expertise in the management of autism or paediatric sleep medicine
- be used in conjunction with non-pharmacological interventions
- be regularly reviewed to evaluate the ongoing need for a pharmacological intervention and to ensure that the benefits continue to outweigh the side effects and risks (10).

Immunoglobulins

Introduction

Immunoglobulins are substances derived from human blood plasma. The plasma, processed from donated human blood, contains antibodies that protect the body against diseases.

Immunoglobulins include intravenous immunoglobulin (IVIg), gamma-globulin or immune serum globulin, which are normally injected into the patient.

Immunoglobulins

Definition: drugs used to treat immune conditions.

Aims: to improve behaviour by treating immune deficiencies.

Who: people with autism of all ages and all levels of ability.

Evidence: very limited evidence that immunoglobulins do not bring any benefits.

Risks: usually minor, but can include kidney failure.

Immunoglobulins are used to treat patients with immune conditions (53).

Aims

Some people think that some of the core features of autism and some of the associated conditions (such as gastrointestinal problems) are caused by immune deficiencies.

They think that using injections or infusions of immunoglobulins can overcome those immunological deficiencies, which will in turn lead to other improvements. For example, some people think that it can lead to improvements in behaviour, such as eye contact and social interaction (54).

Evidence

No high quality research evidence shows that immunoglobulin therapy has any effect on the core features of autism or on any immune problems in people on the autism spectrum.

Immunoglobulin therapy has no effect on bowel disorders in individuals on the autism spectrum according an extremely limited amount of research evidence of sufficiently high quality (55).

Risks

IVIg treatment is usually well-tolerated, that is, usually no major side effects occur. Most adverse effects are mild and are usually related to the rate of infusion. However, according to the American Society of Health-System Pharmacists (2003) IVIg can cause a number of significant, life-threatening hazards including kidney failure, and it also carries the risk of potentially fatal transmission of blood-borne pathogens (56).

Opioid antagonists

Introduction

Opioid antagonists are drugs used to treat conditions such as alcohol dependence and opioid dependence.

Opioid antagonists include naltrexone (ReVia®) and naloxone (Narcan®).

Opioid antagonists appear to work by blocking opioid endorphins (substances in our bodies which produce 'highs' in mood, such as when we exercise vigorously) (57).

Aims

Some people think that some individuals on the autism spectrum have excessive amounts of endorphins in their brains.

> ### Opioid antagonists
>
> **Definition:** drugs used to treat conditions such as alcohol dependence.
>
> **Aims:** to reduce challenging behaviours by blocking opioid endorphins.
>
> **Who:** people with autism of all ages and all levels of ability.
>
> **Evidence:** insufficient evidence to determine if opioid antagonists have any benefits.
>
> **Risks:** significant, including liver damage.

They think that this imbalance can lead to a range of problems, such as self-injury, hyperactivity and ritualistic behaviour. They think that taking opioid antagonists can be used to reduce those behaviours by blocking the endorphins (58).

Evidence

Determining the benefits of opioid antagonists for individuals on the autism spectrum is not currently possible. We must wait for further research of sufficiently high quality to be completed (59).

Risks

Different opioid antagonists carry different risks. For example, according to the American Society of Health-System Pharmacists:

'Naltrexone may cause liver damage when taken in large doses. It is not likely that naltrexone will cause liver damage when taken in recommended doses.'

In addition, naltrexone can cause a number of other side effects including nausea, vomiting, and stomach pain or cramping (60).

Stimulant medications

Introduction

Stimulant medications (or central nervous system stimulants) are drugs used to treat conditions such as ADHD, hyperkinetic disorder and narcolepsy.

Stimulant medications include methylphenidate (Ritalin®).

Stimulant medications are believed to work by increasing the amount of dopamine and noradrenaline (neurotransmitters) in the brain. Increasing the amount of these neurotransmitters is believed to improve self-control, attention and concentration (61).

Stimulant medications

Definition: drugs used to treat conditions such as ADHD, hyperkinetic disorder and narcolepsy.

Aims: to decrease hyperactivity and inattention by regulating dopamine and noradrenaline.

Evidence: very limited amount of evidence that methylphenidate may provide some benefits.

Risks: minor, including loss of appetite, sleep problems, irritability.

Aims

Some people think that stimulant medications can be used with some individuals on the autism spectrum to reduce problem behaviours, such as improving inattention, distractibility, hyperactivity, and impulsivity (62).

Evidence

Determining the benefits of most stimulant medications for individuals on the autism spectrum is not currently possible. We must wait for further research of sufficiently high quality to be completed (63).

Methylphenidate may be beneficial for the treatment of hyperactivity, impulsivity and inattention in some children and young people on the autism spectrum according to a very limited amount of research evidence of sufficiently high quality (6, 7).

Risks

Different stimulant medications carry different risks. According to Cortese (2012):

'The most common adverse events associated with the use of psychostimulants in children and adolescents with ASD include: appetite reduction, sleep-onset difficulties, irritability and emotional outburst.' (64)

Additional information

The National Institute for Health and Care Excellence does not offer any specific advice about the use of stimulant medications for individuals on the autism spectrum. However, it does say:

'Offer psychosocial and pharmacological interventions for the management of coexisting mental health or medical problems in children and young people with autism in line with NICE guidance for children and young people, including: attention deficit hyperactivity disorder (ADHD)'. (10)

The NICE guidance on ADHD states that methylphenidate may be an appropriate medication for treating individuals with ADHD but that:

'Drug treatment for ... people with ADHD should always form part of a comprehensive treatment plan that includes psychological, behavioural and educational advice and interventions.' (65)

Further information

In this book: Please see How to use this book (page 11), Chapter 3 (page 38) for information about interventions, Chapter 4 (page 43) for information about how scientists evaluate those interventions, and Section 3 (page 284) for advice on making the decision about whether or not to use a specific intervention.

Websites: Please see www.researchautism.net/medications for information about medications including information about specific medication and details of scientific studies and trials.

References

1. Dictionary.com (2014) *Drug* [online]. Available at: http://dictionary.reference.com/browse/drug (accessed 16 January, 2015).

2. Medicines and Healthcare Products Agency (2014) *What We Regulate*. London: Medicines and Healthcare Products Regulatory Agency.

3. Politte LC, Henry CA & McDougle CJ (2014) Psychopharmacological interventions in autism spectrum disorder. *Harvard Review of Psychiatry* **22** 76–92.

4. Anagnostou E & Hansen R (2011) Medical treatment overview: traditional and novel psycho-pharmacological and complementary and alternative medications. *Current Opinion in Pediatrics* **23** 621–627.

5. British National Formulary (2014) *Haloperidol*. London: BNF.

6. Research Autism (2014) *Risperidone and autism* [online]. Available at: www.researchautism.net/risperidone-and-autism (accessed January 13, 2015).

7. Research Autism (2014) *Methylphenidate and autism* [online]. Available at: www.researchautism.net/methylphenidate-and-autism (accessed January 13, 2015).

8. Research Autism (2014) *Melatonin and autism* [online]. Available at: www.researchautism.net/melatonin-and-autism (accessed January 13, 2015).

9. Research Autism (2014) *Secretin and autism* [online]. Available at: www.researchautism.net/secretin-and-autism (accessed January 13, 2015).

10. National Institute for Health and Care Excellence (2013) *The Management and Support of Children and Young people on the Autism Spectrum*. London: National Institute for Health and Care Excellence.

11. National Institute for Health and Care Excellence (2012) *Autism: Recognition, referral, diagnosis and management of adults on the autism spectrum*. London: National Institute for Health and Care Excellence.

12. Medicines and Healthcare Products Agency (2013) *Antipsychotic Drugs*. London: Medicines and Healthcare Products Regulatory Agency.

13. Office of Dietary Supplements (2011) *Dietary Supplement Fact Sheet: Vitamin B-6*. Bethesda, MD: Office of Dietary Supplements.

14. Mind (2012) *Making Sense of Antipsychotics*. London: Mind.

15. American Society of Health-System Pharmacists (2010) *Clonidine*. U.S. National Library of Medicine.

16. Fankhauser MP, Karumanchi VC, German ML, Yates A & Karumanchi SD (1992) A double-blind, placebo-controlled study of the efficacy of transdermal clonidine in autism. *Journal of Clinical Psychiatry* **53** 77–82.

17. Handen BL, Sahl R & Hardan AY (2008) Guanfacine in children with autism and/or intellectual disabilities. *Journal of Developmental and Behavioral Pediatrics* **29** 303–308.

18. Research Autism (2014) *Alpha 2-adrenergic receptor agonists and autism* [online]. Available at: www.researchautism.net/alpha 2-adrenergic receptor agonists (accessed January 13, 2015).

19. Di Martino A & Tuchman RF (2001) Antiepileptic drugs: affective use in autism spectrum disorders. *Pediatric Neurology* **25** 199–207.

20. Lai M-C, Lombardo MV & Baron-Cohen S (2014) Autism. *Lancet* **383** 896–910.

21. Hirota T, Veenstra-Vanderweele J, Hollander E & Kishi T (2014) Antiepileptic medications in autism spectrum disorder: a systematic review and meta-analysis. *Journal of Autism and Developmental Disorders* **44** 948–57.

22. Research Autism (2014) *Anticonvulsants and autism* [online]. Available at: www.researchautism.net/anticonvulsants-and-autism (accessed January 13, 2015).

23. American Society of Health-System Pharmacists (2013) *Valproic Acid*. Bethesda, MD: American Society of Health-Case Pharmacists.

24. Royal College of Psychiatrists (2014) *Antidepressants*. London: Royal College of Psychiatrists.

25. Mind (2012) *Antidepressants*. London: Mind.

26. Williams K & Wheeler D (2013) Selective serotonin reuptake inhibitors (SSRIs) for autism spectrum disorders (ASD). *Cochrane Database of Systematic Reviews* **8**.

27. Research Autism (2014) *Antidepressants and autism* [online]. Available at: www.researchautism.net/antidepressants-and-autism (accessed January 13, 2015).

28. American Society of Health-System Pharmacists (2012) *Citalopram*. Bethesda, MD: American Society of Health-Case Pharmacists.

29. Royal College of Psychiatrists (2012) *Antipsychotics*. London: Royal College of Psychiatrists.

30. Posey D, Stigler K, Erickson CA & McDougle CJ (2008) Antipsychotics in the treatment of autism. *The Journal of Clinical Investigation* **118** 6–14.

31. Research Autism (2014) *Antipsychotics and autism* [online]. Available at: www.researchautism.net/antipsychotics-and-autism (accessed January 13, 2015).

32. British National Formulary (2014) *Hypnotics and Anxiolytics*. London: BNF.

33. British National Formulary (2014) *Benzodiazepines*. London: BNF.

34. Buitelaar JK, van der Gaag RJ & van der Hoeven J (1998) Buspirone in the management of anxiety and irritability in children with pervasive developmental disorders: Results of an open-label study. *Journal of Clinical Psychiatry* **59** 56–59.

35. Research Autism (2014) *Anxiolytics and autism* [online]. Available at: www.researchautism.net/anxiolytics (accessed January 13, 2015).

36. British National Formulary (2014) *Diazepam*. London: BNF.

37. Ward F, Tharian P, Roy M, Deb S & Unwin GL (2013) Efficacy of beta blockers in the management of problem behaviours in people with intellectual disabilities: a systematic review. *Research in Developmental Disabilities* **34** 4293–303.

38. Beversdorf D, Saklayen S, Higgins KF, Bodner KE, Kanne SM & Christ SE (2011) Effect of propranolol on word fluency in autism. *Cognitive and Behavioral Neurology* **24** 11–17.

39. Research Autism (2014) *Betablockers and autism* [online]. Available at: www.researchautism.net/betablockers (accessed January 13, 2015).

40. British National Formulary (2014) *Beta-adrenoceptor Blocking Drugs*. London: BNF.

41. Lee YJ, Oh SH, Park C, Hong M, Lee AR, Yoo HJ, Shin CY, Cheon KA & Bahn GH (2014) Advanced pharmacotherapy evidenced by pathogenesis of autism spectrum disorder. *Clinical Psychopharmacology and Neuroscience* **12** 19–30.

42. Handen BL, Johnson CR, McAuliffe-Bellin S, Murray PJ & Hardan AY (2011) Safety and efficacy of donepezil in children and adolescents with autism: neuropsychological measures. *Journal of Child and Adolescent Psychopharmacology* **21** 43–50.

43. Research Autism (2014) *Cholineserase inhibitors and autism* [online]. Available at: www.researchautism.net/cholinesterase-inhibitors (accessed January 13, 2015).

44. American Society of Health-System Pharmacists (2008) *Donepezil*. Bethesda, MD: American Society of Health-Case Pharmacists.

45. US National Library of Medicine (2014) *Hormones*. Bethesda, MD: US National Library of Medicine.

46. Rossignol DA & Frye RE (2011) Melatonin in autism spectrum disorders: a systematic review and meta-analysis. *Developmental Medicine and Child Neurology* **53** 783–792.

47. Anagnostou E, Soorya L, Brian J, Dupuis A, Mankad D, Smile S & Jacob S (2014) Intranasal oxytocin in the treatment of autism spectrum disorders: a review of literature and early safety and efficacy data in youth. *Brain Research*.

48. Krishnaswami S, McPheeters ML & Veenstra-Vanderweele J (2011) A systematic review of secretin for children with autism spectrum disorders. *Pediatrics* **127** e1322–5.

49. Research Autism (2014) *Oxytocin and autism* [online]. Available at: www.researchautism.net/oxytocin-and-autism (accessed January 13, 2015).

50. American Society of Health-System Pharmacists (2010) *Melatonin*. Bethesda, MD: American Society of Health-Case Pharmacists.

51. University of Maryland Medical Center (2010) *Oxytocin*. Baltimore, MD: University of Maryland Medical Center.

52. WebMD (2009) *Secretin* [online]. WebMD.

53. Emedicinehealth (2010) *Immunoglobulin* [online]. Emedicinehealth.

54. Gupta S, Samra D & Agrawal S (2010) Adaptive and innate immune responses in autism: rationale for therapeutic use of intravenous immunoglobulin. *Journal of Clinical Immunology* **30** 90–96.

55. Research Autism (2014) *Immune globulins and autism* [online]. Available at: www.researchautism.net/immune-globulins-and-autism (accessed January 13, 2015).

56. American Society of Health-System Pharmacists (2003) *Immune Globulin Intravenous Injection*. Bethesda, MD: American Society of Health-Case Pharmacists.

57. Netdoctor (2007) *Naloxone* [online]. London: Hearst Magazines.

58. ElChaar GM, Maisch NM, Augusto LMG & Wehring HJ (2006) Efficacy and safety of naltrexone use in pediatric patients with autistic disorder. *The Annals of Pharmacotherapy* **40** 1086–95.

59. Research Autism (2014) *Opioid antagonists and autism* [online]. Available at: www.researchautism.net/opioid-antagonists (accessed January 13, 2015).

60. American Society of Health-System Pharmacists (2009) *Naltrexone*. Bethesda, MD: American Society of Health-Case Pharmacists.

61. WebMD (2014) *Stimulant drugs for ADHD* [online]. WebMD.

62. Research Units on Pediatric Psychopharmacology (RUPP) Autism Network (2005) Randomized, controlled, crossover trial of methylphenidate in pervasive developmental disorders with hyperactivity. *Archives of General Psychiatry* **62** 1266–1274.

63. Research Autism (2014) *Stimulants and related medications and autism* [online]. Available at: www.researchautism.net/stimulant-and-related-medications (accessed January 13, 2015).

64. Cortese S, Castelnau P, Morcillo C, Roux S & Bonnet-Brilhault F (2012) Psychostimulants for ADHD-like symptoms in individuals with autism spectrum disorders. *Expert Review of Neurotherapeutics* **12** 461–73.

65. National Institute for Health and Care Excellence (2000) *Methylphenidate, Atomoxetine and Dexamfetamine for the Treatment of Attention Deficit Hyperactivity Disorder in Children and Adolescents (including a review of guidance TA13)*. London: National Institute for Health and Care Excellence.

Chapter 18:
Special diets

Introduction

Special diets are diets which have been modified in some way to bring about specific healthcare benefits. Most special diets used to help people on the autism spectrum are 'exclusion' diets. This means you avoid or reduce foodstuffs which may harm you (such as additives in the additive-free diet). Other examples of special diets are the gluten-free, casein-free diet, and the salicylate-free diet.

In some diets you have to exclude some foodstuffs but include others, such as the specific carbohydrate diet. This excludes complex carbohydrates (such as those found in rice and potatoes) and replaces them with simple carbohydrates (such as those found in bananas and squashes).

In practice, many diets share similar characteristics. For example, the Feingold diet is a mixture of the additive-free diet and the salicylate-free diet, while the specific carbohydrate diet incorporates elements of the gluten-free diet (1–3).

Some people think that diet is a key component of any intervention designed to help people on the autism spectrum. Some people also think that modifying the diet and the gastrointestinal system is necessary for the success of other treatments and therefore should come first (4).

Diets are sometimes combined with other therapies. For example, some people advocate following a particular diet, taking one or more dietary supplements and using detoxification techniques such as chelation.

Evidence

Eating a healthy balanced diet is recommended for everybody in order to maintain good health. Anyone with a particular condition (in addition to or separate from autism) may be recommended to follow a special diet by a dietitian and this should be followed

Choosing Autism Interventions: A Research-Based Guide © Research Autism and Autism West Midlands

on an individual basis. For example, dietitians may recommend a gluten or milk exclusion diet for various gut problems.

Most special diets provide the same benefits for people on the autism spectrum as they do to people who are not on the autism spectrum. They do not appear to provide any additional benefits to people on the autism spectrum, according to a limited amount of research evidence of sufficiently high quality.

No evidence at all supports the use of most special diets (such as additive-free diets, the specific-carbohydrate diet, and the yeast-free diet) (5, 6, 7).

Determining the benefits of other diets (such as the gluten-free, casein-free diet or the ketogenic diet) for people on the autism spectrum is not currently possible. We must wait until further research of sufficiently high quality has been completed (8, 9).

NICE guidelines

The National Institute for Health and Care Excellence (NICE) made the following observations on the use of exclusion diets for adults on the autism spectrum:

'... there is very little evidence regarding safety and efficacy for exclusion diets ... for the treatment of autism.' (10)

Supply, quality and regulation

The supply and availability of the ingredients required for special diets varies enormously between different diets and sometimes between different countries. For example, obtaining gluten-free or casein-free ingredients can be difficult in some countries.

The quality of special diets varies enormously depending on the diet, the ingredients used, and how rigorously you follow the diet. Most specialist diets are unregulated and uncontrolled, since anyone can choose to follow them.

Various support groups exist which may be able to advise you on how to follow specific diets and there are usually resources (such as books or DVDs) which may also instruct you on how to follow those diets.

However, if you are contemplating following a special diet, you should seek advice from a paediatrician, GP or dietitian. The British Dietetic Association has information about qualified dietitians in the UK.

Costs and time

The cost of following a special diet depends on things like the type of diet, whether the whole family is following the diet, whether you are buying ready-made meals or making them yourself.

For example, according to the *Canadian Journal of Dietetic Practice and Research*, gluten-free products were on average 242% more expensive than regular gluten containing products (11).

Most special diets are designed to be followed seven days a week for months or years. The amount of time you need each week will depend on the type of diet and whether you are making all of the meals yourself. In addition, it takes time to check the labels of foods you buy to ensure that they do not contain restricted foodstuffs.

Risks and safety

Many potential risks lie in wait when withdrawing normal or regular foods from individuals, but especially young children.

Some individuals on the autism spectrum are faddy eaters. They already have a less healthy and less varied diet than other people. Restricting what they eat even further may reinforce those rigid eating patterns. It may also increase their social isolation (because they can't eat the same food as their peers at parties or restaurants).

In the long-term special diets could lead to health problems if they are not carefully balanced. For example, according to one review:

'The combination of food selectivity and restrictive diets can make it difficult to achieve an adequate diet, consequently resulting in an excessive intake of certain foods and/or deficiencies and malnutrition due to insufficient amounts of other foods. In turn, inadequate intakes may lead to the development of chronic and degenerative conditions that tend to appear in the third or fourth decade of life (cardiovascular disease, high blood pressure, diabetes, dyslipidemia, and osteoporosis, among others) or even earlier, in the case of menstrual disturbances, sleep apnea, and psychosocial disorders.' (12)

Individuals with autism or their carers who have concerns about their or their child's diet should seek advice from a responsible health professional such as their health visitor or GP. This may lead to a referral to a dietitian, in particular one with experience of working with individuals with autism.

Specific diets

Additive-free diets

Introduction

Additive-free diets are exclusion diets which require you to avoid artificial additives such as colourings, flavourings and preservatives.

Additive-free diets are based on the idea that some additives contain harmful chemicals which can damage the brain.

Some additive-free diets, such as the Feingold diet, also exclude other substances such as salicylates (a group of substances that are toxic to insects and found in all plants) in the belief that these also cause stress to the digestion (13).

> ### Additive-free diets
>
> **Definition:** a type of diet that excludes artificial colourings, flavourings and preservatives.
>
> **Aims:** to avoid consumption of additives, leading to improvements in mental and physical health.
>
> **Who:** people with autism of all ages and all levels of ability.
>
> **Evidence:** none.
>
> **Risks:** no significant risks.

Aims

Various people have made claims about different additive-free diets. For example, the Feingold Association of the United States claims that the Feingold diet can be used to treat people with a wide range of conditions including autism and ADHD.

It also claims that the diet can be used to help tackle a wide range of mental and physical health problems, including gastrointestinal problems and sleep disturbances (13).

Evidence

No evidence shows that artificial additives (or salicylates) are especially harmful to people on the autism spectrum.

No evidence shows that an additive-free diet (such as the Feingold diet) has any specific benefits for people on the autism spectrum (5). However the NHS advises that all children should avoid additives that can cause hyperactive behaviour (14).

Risks

No specific risks are associated with following additive-free diets other than those associated with any special diet.

Gluten-free, casein-free diet

Introduction

The gluten-free, casein-free diet (GFCF diet) involves avoiding all foodstuffs which contain gluten and casein.

Gluten is a protein found in some cereals such as wheat, rye and barley (15). Oats contain a similar protein and are usually processed in the same factories, so are often included in this diet (16). Casein is a protein found in dairy products such as milk, butter, cheese and yoghurt.

Some people think that autistic people are unable to digest gluten and casein

Gluten-free, casein-free diet

Definition: a diet which avoids all foodstuffs containing gluten and casein.

Aims: to avoid the creation of harmful peptides, leading to improvements in IQ, communication and social skills.

Who: people with autism of all ages and all levels of ability.

Evidence: insufficient research evidence to determine if the gluten-free, casein-free diet has any benefits.

Risks: minor risks including possible nutritional deficiencies and stigmatisation from activities such as attending restaurants or parties.

properly and that any undigested gluten and casein (in the form of harmful peptides) enter the central nervous system and damage the brain (4).

Aims

Some people think that the gluten-free, casein-free diet is suitable for individuals with autism of all ages but is most effective with pre-adolescent children.

They think that removing or reducing gluten and casein will lead to improvements in areas such as IQ, communication and social skills (17).

Evidence

Determining if individuals on the autism spectrum have unusual amounts of peptides in the central nervous system or that this causes behavioural and other problems is not currently possible. We must wait until further research of sufficiently high quality has been completed.

Determining if the GFCF diet has any significant benefits for individuals on the autism spectrum is not currently possible. We must wait until further research of sufficiently high quality has been completed (8).

Risks

The gluten-free, casein-free diet poses a number of potential risks including a low intake of calcium, iodine and fibre which can lead to weaker bones, iodine deficiency and gut problems (there is also a risk of masking undiagnosed coeliac disease if a coeliac disease test is not carried out before trialling the diet) (18).

Ketogenic diet

Introduction

The ketogenic diet is a low-carbohydrate diet designed to mimic many of the biochemical changes associated with prolonged starvation.

It is used for the treatment of intractable seizures, that is, seizures which have not responded to normal anticonvulsant medications and therapies.

How the diet is supposed to work is still unclear (19).

Aims

Some people think that the ketogenic diet is suitable for people with both autism and epilepsy who have not responded to traditional epilepsy medication.

They think that the ketogenic diet can be used to improve a range of behaviours in children on the autism spectrum including hyperactivity, social interaction and social communication (19).

> ## Ketogenic diet
>
> **Definition:** a high-fat, adequate-protein, low-carbohydrate diet.
>
> **Aims:** to reduce problem behaviours through ketosis.
>
> **Who:** people with both autism and epilepsy who have not responded to epilepsy medication.
>
> **Evidence:** insufficient evidence to determine the benefits for people with autism.
>
> **Risks:** significant, including delayed growth, gastrointestinal symptoms and kidney stones.

Evidence

Determining the benefits of the ketogenic diet for people on the autism spectrum is not currently possible. We must wait until further research of sufficiently high quality has been completed (9).

Risks

The ketogenic diet may produce a number of serious, adverse side effects including growth retardation, gastrointestinal symptoms, carnitine deficiency, kidney stones, and elevated lipids according to Kossoff *et al*. More seriously 'Children receiving the ketogenic diet continuously for more than six years are at high risk for kidney stones, bone fractures, and growth disturbances' (20).

Additional information

According to Evangeliou:

'The classic ketogenic diet is very restrictive and requires a large amount of dietetic involvement in terms of calculations, monitoring, patient support, and motivation from the family to adhere to the diet; consequently, it is difficult to adapt for children with [learning disabilities].' (19)

Specific-carbohydrate diet

Introduction

The specific carbohydrate diet excludes complex carbohydrates (such as those found in rice and potatoes) and replaces them with simple carbohydrates (such as those found in bananas and squashes).

The diet also uses fermented products, such as homemade yogurt, which is supposed to repopulate the gut with beneficial yeasts and bacteria.

Specific carbohydrate diet

Definition: a diet which excludes complex carbohydrates and replaces them with simple carbohydrates.

Aims: to improve behaviour by improving the functioning of the gut.

Who: people with autism of all ages and all levels of ability.

Evidence: no evidence for its use in people with autism.

Risks: significant, including nutritional deficiencies.

The diet is designed to remove complex carbohydrates which are supposed to feed harmful fungi and bacteria.

The diet is sometimes used to treat people with a variety of gastrointestinal disorders, including irritable bowel syndrome (IBS), inflammatory bowel disease (IBD), ulcerative colitis (UC), Crohn's disease, and coeliac disease (21).

Aims

Some people think that the specific carbohydrate diet is suitable for anyone on the autism spectrum with gastrointestinal problems.

They think that the specific carbohydrate diet can restore normal gut functioning in people on the autism spectrum. They also think that this can lead to a range of improvements such as improvements in behaviour (22).

Evidence

No evidence shows that the specific carbohydrate diet is helpful to people on the autism spectrum (6).

Risks

The specific-carbohydrate diet (SCD) presents some potential risks. For example, according to Zelman:

'This can be a very challenging diet to follow because there are a limited number of foods allowed... Not only is the SCD difficult to follow, it may also be risky for your health. When you eliminate whole food groups like dairy and grains, you significantly reduce the nutritional quality of the diet, which may result in nutritional deficiencies.' (21)

Further information

In this book: Please see How to use this book (page 11), Chapter 3 (page 38) for information about interventions, Chapter 4 (page 43) for information about how scientists evaluate those interventions, and Section 3 (page 284) for advice on making the decision about whether or not to use a specific intervention.

Websites: Please see www.researchautism.net/special-diets for information about special diets including information about specific diets and details of scientific studies and trials.

References

1. IAN Network (2008) *IAN research Findings: Special diets*. Baltimore, MD: IAN Network.

2. Marti LF (2013) Dietary interventions in children with autism spectrum disorders – an updated review of the research evidence. *Current Clinical Pharmacology* **9** 335–349.

3. Geraghty ME, Bates-Wall J, Ratliff-Schaub K & Lane AE (2010) Nutritional interventions and therapies in autism – a spectrum of what we know: part 2. *ICAN: Infant, Child & Adolescent Nutrition* **2** 120–133.

4. Kidd PM (2002) Autism, an extreme challenge to integrative medicine. Part 2: medical management. *Alternative Medicine Review: A Journal of Clinical Therapeutic* **7** 472–499.

5. Research Autism (2014) *Feingold diet and autism* [online]. Available at: www.researchautism.net/feingold-diet-and-autism (accessed January 13, 2015).

6. Research Autism (2014) *Specific carbohydrate diet and autism* [online]. Available at: www.researchautism.net/specific-carbohydrate-diet-and-autism (accessed January 13, 2015).

7. Research Autism (2014) *Yeast-free diet and autism* [online]. Available at: www.researchautism.net/yeast-free-diet (accessed January 13, 2015).

8. Research Autism (2014) *Gluten-free, casein-free diet and autism* [online]. Available at: www.researchautism.net/gluten-free-casein-free-diet-and-autism (accessed January 13, 2015).

9. Research Autism (2014) *Ketogenic diet and autism* [online]. Available at: www.researchautism.net/ketogenic-diet-and-autism (accessed January 13, 2015).

10. National Institute for Health and Care Excellence (2012) *Autism: Recognition, referral, diagnosis and management of adults on the autism spectrum*. London: National Institute for Health and Care Excellence.

11. Stevens L & Rashid M (2008) Gluten-free and regular foods: a cost comparison. *Canadian Journal of Dietetic Practice and Research* **69** 147–150.

12. Marí-Bauset S, Zazpe I, Marí-Sanchis A, Llopis-González A & Suárez-Varela MM (2015) Anthropometric measurements and nutritional assessment in autism spectrum disorders: a systematic review. *Research in Autism Spectrum Disorders* **9** 130–143.

13. Feingold Association of the United States (2008) *Overview [of the Feingold Diet]*. Riverhead, NY: Feingold Association of the United States.

14. NHS Choices (2012) *Food Colours and Hyperactivity*. London, UK: NHS.

15. Jaret P (2011) *The Truth about Gluten*. New York, NY: WebMD.

16. Thompson T (2004) Gluten contamination of commercial oat products in the United States. *New England Journal of Medicine* **351** 2021–2022.

17. Mulloy A, Lang R, O'Reilly M, Sigafoos J, Lancioni G & Rispoli M (2010) Gluten-free and casein-free diets in the treatment of autism spectrum disorders: a systematic review. *Research in Autism Spectrum Disorders* **4** 328–339.

18. Connor Z (2014) Autism spectrum disorder. In V Shaw and M Lawson (eds) *Clinical Paediatric Dietetics* (4th edition). Oxford: Wiley-Blackwell. pp 504–522.

19. Evangeliou A, Vlachonikolis I, Mihailidou H, Spilioti M, Skarpalezou A, Makaronas N, Prokopiou A, Christodoulou P, Liapi-Adamidou G, Helidonis E, Sbyrakis S & Smeitink J (2003) Application of a ketogenic diet in children with autistic behavior: pilot study. *Journal of Child Neurology* **18** 113–118.

20. Kossoff EH, Zupec-Kania BA & Rho JM (2009) Ketogenic diets: an update for child neurologists. *Journal of Child Neurology* **24** 979–88.

21. Zelman KM (2011) *Special Carbohydrate Diet: Diet review*. WebMD.

22. Pecanbread.com (undated) *Introducing SCD* [online]. Available at: http://pecanbread.com/p/intro/introhome.html (accessed 16 January, 2015).

Chapter 19:
Dietary supplements

Introduction

Dietary supplements (also called nutritional supplements) are intended to correct nutritional deficiencies.

Dietary supplements include vitamins, minerals, herbals and botanicals, amino acids, enzymes, and many other products. They come in a variety of forms including tablets, capsules, and powders, as well as drinks and energy bars (1, 2).

Some people think that some individuals on the autism spectrum have a range of nutritional and metabolic problems. These include low levels of nutrients, high levels of oxidative stress (a chemical state within cells that can increase cellular damage) and difficulties with metabolic processes (such as digestion).

Some people think that these nutritional and metabolic differences may be the cause of some of the core features of autism (such as impaired communication and social difficulties) and related issues (such as challenging behaviours).

They also think that some of these problems can be overcome by taking one or more dietary supplements, sometimes in combination with other therapies, such as special diets (3, 4).

Evidence

Eating a healthy and varied diet is important for good health. Food and drinks provide a range of nutrients and all vitamins and essential minerals are just that – essential for good health. If too little of any of these nutrients is consumed, nutrient deficiencies can occur, which cause ill health. Consuming too much of any of these nutrients can also cause poor health. It is unusual to consume too much via foods, however taking dietary supplements with high levels of nutrients does carry a risk of nutrient overload. Some diseases (such as cystic fibrosis), some conditions (such as cerebral palsy) and other factors (such as breast-feeding) increase an individual's needs for some nutrients (5, 6).

Some evidence shows that some individuals on the autism spectrum may have nutritional and metabolic problems. However, the number of individuals on the autism spectrum who have these problems is not clear. It is also not clear whether these problems or differences are any more common in individuals on the autism spectrum than in other individuals. Possibly, these problems cause or worsen symptoms (of autism or related issues). Or maybe they arise because of autism, or they could be completely unrelated to autism. Nobody knows (7).

Most dietary supplements provide the same benefits for people on the autism spectrum as they do to people who are not on the autism spectrum. They do not appear to provide any additional benefits to people on the autism spectrum, according to a limited amount of research evidence of sufficiently high quality. Some dietary supplements may make some problems worse for some children and young people on the autism spectrum according to a limited amount of research evidence of sufficiently high quality (8, 9).

NICE guidance

The National Institute for Health and Care Excellence (NICE) reported that some dietary supplements may have some limited benefits for some children and young people on the autism spectrum beyond the benefits provided to other people. However it also reported that:

'... the evidence was very limited and further randomised placebo-controlled studies are required to corroborate the existing evidence for ... dietary supplements in children and young people with autism.' (8)

NICE made the following observations on the use of dietary supplements for adults on the autism spectrum:

'... there is very little evidence regarding safety and efficacy for... vitamins, minerals or supplements for the treatment of autism. Moreover, it is important to bear in mind that ... some dietary supplements can be associated with adverse side effects and/or interact and perhaps interfere with the action of other supplements or prescribed drugs.' (9)

Supply, quality and regulation

The quality of dietary supplements can vary enormously depending on the manufacturer, the ingredients and manufacturing process.

In the UK, the quality of dietary supplements is regulated by the Medicines and Healthcare Products Regulatory Agency if they 'contain a pharmacologically active substance or make medicinal claims (claims to treat or prevent disease, or to interfere with the normal operation of a physiological function of the human body) ...' (10).

In the USA, dietary supplements are not classed as drugs but the Food and Drug Administration is responsible for taking action against any unsafe dietary supplement product after it reaches the market (1).

Doctors will normally refer individuals to registered dietitians to assess an individual's diet and recommend dietary supplements where needed.

Risks and safety

Many dietary supplements contain active ingredients that can have strong effects in the body, so those pose risks. For example, according to the Office of Dietary Supplements:

'... getting too much vitamin A can cause headaches and liver damage, reduce bone strength, and cause birth defects. Excess iron causes nausea and vomiting and may damage the liver and other organs.' (1)

Supplements are most likely to cause side effects or harm when people take them instead of prescribed medicines or when people take several supplements at the same time (1).

Dietary supplements can also interact with certain prescription drugs in ways that can cause problems. For example, vitamin B-6 can reduce the effectiveness of some epilepsy drugs, such as sodium valproate, carbamazepine and phenytoin (11).

Specific dietary supplements

We have included the following dietary supplements because they are in common use among people on the autism spectrum although there are many, many others.

Carnitine

Introduction

Carnitine is the generic term for a group of natural substances that include L-carnitine, acetyl-L-carnitine, and propionyl-L-carnitine.

Carnitine is found in nearly all cells of the body and in certain foodstuffs, such as meat, fish, poultry, and milk.

Carnitine plays a critical role in energy production. It transports long-chain fatty acids into the mitochondria (the 'power stations' inside the cell) so they can be metabolised to produce energy. It also transports the waste products out of the mitochondria to prevent their accumulation (12).

> ### Carnitine
>
> **Definition:** a natural substance that plays a critical role in energy production.
>
> **Aims:** to treat a range of behavioural problems by treating nutritional deficiencies.
>
> **Who:** anyone with autism and nutritional deficiencies.
>
> **Evidence:** insufficient evidence to determine if carnitine has any benefits for people with autism.
>
> **Risks:** minor, including nausea, vomiting, abdominal cramps, diarrhoea.

Aims

Carnitine supplements are sometimes used to treat anyone with autism who is believed to have one or more nutritional or metabolic deficiencies.

Some people think that carnitine can be used to treat a variety of issues in individuals on the autism spectrum including 'behaviour, cognition, socialisation, and health/physical traits associated with autism diagnosis' (13).

Evidence

Determining the benefits of carnitine supplements for people on the autism spectrum beyond any benefits provided to other people is not currently possible. We must wait for further research of sufficiently high quality to be completed (14).

Risks and safety

According to the Office of Dietary Supplements: 'At doses of approximately 3g/day, carnitine supplements can cause nausea, vomiting, abdominal cramps, diarrhoea, and a "fishy" body odour. Rarer side effects include muscle weakness in uremic patients and seizures in those with seizure disorders' (12).

Dimethylglycine

Introduction

Dimethylglycine (DMG) is a constituent of many important substances in the body, including amino acids, hormones and neurotransmitters.

It also appears to play an important role in the brain and in the immune system.

It is found naturally in plant and animal cells and certain foods are good sources, such as beans and liver (15).

Aims

Dimethylglycine

Definition: a constituent of many important substances in the body.

Aims: to treat a range of behavioural problems by treating nutritional deficiencies.

Who: anyone with autism and nutritional deficiencies.

Evidence: extremely limited evidence that dimethylglycine does not provide any benefits.

Risks: none, provided recommended daily allowances are followed.

DMG supplements are sometimes used to treat anyone with autism who is believed to have one or more nutritional or metabolic deficiencies.

Some people think that DMG supplements can cause a range of behavioural improvements in people on the autism spectrum including improved behaviour, better eye contact, and improved speech (16).

Evidence

DMG does not provide any benefits for individuals on the autism spectrum beyond any benefits provided to other people according to an extremely limited amount of research evidence of sufficiently high quality (16).

Risks and safety

No risks exist when taking DMG supplements at the doses recommended within the US. There are no recommended doses within the UK (15).

Multivitamin/mineral supplements

Introduction

Multivitamin/mineral supplements (MVMs) contain a combination of vitamins and minerals, and sometimes other ingredients as well.

Many types of multivitamin/mineral supplements are on the market. Manufacturers choose which vitamins, minerals, and other ingredients, as well as their amounts, to include in their products (17).

Aims

Multivitamin/mineral supplements are sometimes used to treat anyone on the autism spectrum who is believed to have one or more nutritional deficiencies.

Some people think that multivitamin/mineral supplements bring a range of benefits to people on the autism spectrum, including

---

Multivitamin/mineral supplements

Definition: supplements which contain a combination of vitamins and minerals.

Aims: to treat a range of behavioural problems by treating nutritional deficiencies.

Who: anyone with autism and nutritional deficiencies.

Evidence: insufficient evidence to determine if multivitamin/mineral supplements have any benefits.

Risks: none, provided recommended daily allowances are followed.

a reduction in challenging behaviours and improved social communication (18).

Evidence

NICE recommends some multivitamin supplements for some groups of people who are at risk of deficiency. For example, it recommends that:

'All children aged six months to five years should take a supplement containing vitamins A, C and D. This is a precaution because growing children may not get enough, especially those not eating a varied diet, such as fussy eaters.' (19)

Determining the benefits of multivitamin/mineral supplements for individuals on the autism spectrum beyond any benefits provided to other people is not currently possible. We must wait for further research of sufficiently high quality to be completed (20).

Risks and safety

According to the Office of Dietary Supplements: 'Taking a basic MVM that provides nutrients approximating recommended intakes should pose no safety risks to healthy people' (17).

Omega-3 fatty acids

Introduction

Omega-3 fatty acids are essential fatty acids, that is, essential to good health.

Omega-3 fatty acids cannot be created within the human body and must therefore be obtained from foodstuffs, such as some plant seeds and fish oil.

Omega-3 fatty acids are important for a number of bodily functions, including muscle activity, blood clotting, digestion, fertility, cell division and cell growth (21).

Aims

Some people think that some individuals on the autism spectrum have too little omega-3 and too much omega-6 in their bodies. They think that this imbalance can lead to a range of problems in people on the autism spectrum.

They think that taking omega-3 supplements can lead to a range of benefits including improvements to overall health, social interaction and communication (22).

> ## Omega-3 fatty acids
>
> **Definition:** a group of essential fatty acids.
>
> **Aims:** to treat behavioural problems by changing the ratio of omega-3 to omega-6 in the body.
>
> **Who:** anyone with autism and insufficient omega-3 fatty acids.
>
> **Evidence:** insufficient evidence to determine if omega-3 fatty acids have any benefits for people with autism.
>
> **Risks:** minor gastrointestinal symptoms, such as belching, indigestion, or diarrhoea.

Evidence

According to the NHS Choices website: 'Omega-3 fatty acids, primarily those found in oily fish, can help maintain a healthy heart and reduce the risk of heart disease when eaten as part of a healthy diet.' (23)

Determining the benefits of omega-3 supplements for individuals on the autism spectrum beyond any benefits provided to other people is not currently possible. We must wait for further research of sufficiently high quality to be completed (24).

Risks and safety

According to the NHS Choices website: 'If you take fish liver oil supplements, remember these are high in vitamin A. This is because fish store vitamin A in their livers. Having too much vitamin A over many years could be harmful. The Scientific Advisory Committee on Nutrition advises that if you take supplements containing vitamin A, you should not have more than a total of 1.5mg a day from your food and supplements combined'. (25)

According to the NHS Choices website: 'Omega-3 supplements may also be unsuitable for people with certain conditions and may interact with some medicines including those that control high blood pressure. If you are thinking of taking a fish oil supplement, it's best to speak to your doctor' (26).

Probiotics and prebiotics

Introduction

Probiotics are live micro-organisms (such as bacteria) thought to be beneficial to human health.

Prebiotics are natural substances (non-digestible carbohydrates) found in some foods and are supposed to encourage the growth of probiotics.

Commonly used probiotics include Lactobacillus and Bifidobacterium, each of which includes specific types of bacteria.

> ### Probiotic and prebiotics
> **Definition:** live micro-organisms thought to be beneficial to human health.
>
> **Aims:** to treat behavioural problems by treating gastrointestinal problems.
>
> **Who:** people with autism and gastrointestinal problems.
>
> **Evidence:** no evidence for the use of probiotics or prebiotics in people with autism.
>
> **Risks:** none, although long-term effects are unknown.

Probiotics are commonly used to treat gastrointestinal problems such as diarrhoea, irritable bowel syndrome, and inflammatory bowel diseases (such as ulcerative colitis and Crohn's disease) (27).

Aims

Prebiotics and probiotics are sometimes given to individuals on the autism spectrum with gastrointestinal problems.

Some people think that taking probiotics or prebiotics can restore normal gut functioning, which will in turn lead to behavioural improvements (28).

Evidence

According to the British Dietitians Association: 'Many probiotics have been shown to restore the balance of the gut bacteria and in doing so can help our body function optimally in a number of ways.' (29)

No research evidence shows that probiotics or prebiotics have any benefits for people on the autism spectrum beyond any benefits provided to other people (30).

Risks and safety

According to the Office of Dietary Supplements, '... probiotics usually have few side effects. However, the data on safety, particularly long-term safety, are limited, and the risk of serious side effects may be greater in people who have underlying health conditions.' (27)

Vitamin B-6

Introduction

Vitamin B-6 is naturally present in many foods (such as beans, nuts and cereals).

It is also added to many other foods and is available as a dietary supplement.

Vitamin B-6 performs a wide variety of functions in the body and is extremely versatile, with involvement in more than a hundred enzyme reactions, mostly concerned with metabolising proteins (11).

Vitamin B-6

Definition: a vitamin found in foodstuffs such as beans, nuts and cereals.

Aims: to treat behavioural problems by addressing nutritional deficiencies.

Who: anyone with autism and vitamin B-6 deficiencies.

Evidence: insufficient evidence to determine if vitamin B-6 has any benefits.

Risks: nerve damage to the arms and legs.

Aims

Vitamin B supplements are sometimes used to treat individuals on the autism spectrum who are believed to have a vitamin B deficiency.

Some people think that taking vitamin B-6 supplements can lead to behavioural improvements in people on the autism spectrum. For example, Nye and Brice reported that, if effective, '... B6-Mg intervention would result in improved verbal skills, non-verbal skills, social interaction skills, and reactions to environmental stimuli and changes.' (31)

Evidence

Determining the benefits of vitamin B-6 supplements for people on the autism spectrum beyond any benefits provided to other people is not currently possible. We must wait for further research of sufficiently high quality to be completed (32).

Risks and safety

According to the NHS Choices website: 'You should be able to get the vitamin B-6 you need by eating a varied and balanced diet. If you take vitamin B-6 supplements, do not take too much because this could be harmful. Do not take more than 10mg of vitamin B-6 a day in supplements, unless advised to by a doctor.' (33)

According to the Office of Dietary Supplements: 'Too much vitamin B-6 can result in nerve damage to the arms and legs. This neuropathy is usually related to high intake of vitamin B-6 from supplements, and is reversible when supplementation is stopped.' (11)

Further information

In this book: Please see How to use this book (page 11), Chapter 3 (page 38) for information about interventions, Chapter 4 (page 43) for information about how scientists evaluate those interventions, and Section 3 (page 284) for advice on making the decision about whether or not to use a specific intervention.

Websites: Please see www.researchautism.net/diets-and-supplements for information about dietary supplements including information about specific supplements and details of scientific studies and trials.

References

1. Office of *Dietary Supplements (2011) Dietary Supplements: What you need to know*. Bethesda, MD: Office of Dietary Supplements.

2. Office of Dietary Supplements (2006) *Dietary Supplements: Background information*. Bethesda, MD: Office of Dietary Supplements.

3. IAN Network (undated) *Vitamins and Supplements*. Baltimore, MD: IAN Network.

4. Kawicka A & Regulska-Ilow B (2013) How nutritional status, diet and dietary supplements can affect autism. A review. *Roczniki Pa_stwowego Zak_adu Higieny* **64** 1–12.

5. Shaw V & Lawson M (Eds) (2007) *Clinical Paediatric Dietetics* (3rd edition). Oxford: Wiley-Blackwell.

6. Gandy J (Eds) (2014) *Manual of Dietetic Practice* (5th edition). Oxford: Wiley-Blackwell.

7. IAN Network (2010) *Mitochondrial Disease and Autism*. Baltimore, MD: IAN Network.

8. National Institute for Health and Care Excellence (2013) *The Management and Support of Children and Young People on the Autism Spectrum*. London: National Institute for Health and Care Excellence.

9. National Institute for Health and Care Excellence (2012) *Autism: Recognition, referral, diagnosis and management of adults on the autism spectrum*. London: National Institute for Health and Care Excellence.

10. Medicines and Healthcare Products Agency (2013) *Borderline Products*. London: Medicines and Healthcare Products Regulatory Agency.

11. Office of Dietary Supplements (2011) *Dietary Supplement Fact sheet: Vitamin B-6*. Bethesda, MD: Office of Dietary Supplements.

12. Office of Dietary Supplements (2013) *Carnitine*. Bethesda, MD: Office of Dietary Supplements.

13. Fahmy SF, El-hamamsy MH, Zaki OK & Badary OA (2013) l-Carnitine supplementation improves the behavioral symptoms in autistic children. *Research in Autism Spectrum Disorders* **7** 159–166.

14. Research Autism (2014) *Carnitine and autism* [online]. Available at: www.researchautism.net/carnitine (accessed January 13, 2015).

15. WebMD (2011) *Dimethylglycine*. New York, NY: WebMD.

16. Research Autism (2014) *Dimethylglycine and autism* [online]. Available at: www.researchautism.net/dimethylglycine-and-autism (accessed January 13, 2015).

17. Office of Dietary Supplements (2013) *Multivitamin/mineral supplements*. Bethesda, MD: Office of Dietary Supplements.

18. Adams JB, Audhya T, McDonough-Means S, Rubin RA, Quig D, Geis E, Gehn E, Loresto M, Mitchell J, Atwood S, Barnhouse S & Lee W (2011) Effect of a vitamin/mineral supplement on children and adults with autism. *BMC Pediatrics* **11** 111.

19. NHS Choices (2014) *Do I Need Vitamin Supplements?* London, UK: NHS.

20. Research Autism (2014) *Multi vitamin and mineral supplements and autism* [online]. Available at: www.researchautism.net/multi-vitamin-and-mineral-supplements (accessed January 13, 2015).

21. Office of Dietary Supplements (2013) *Omega-3 Supplements: An introduction*. Bethesda, MD: Office of Dietary Supplements.

22. James S, Montgomery P & Williams KJ (2009) Omega-3 fatty acids supplementation for autism spectrum disorders (ASD). *Cochrane Database of Systematic Reviews* **9**.

23. NHS Choices (2013) *The Vegetarian Diet*. London, UK: NHS.

24. Research Autism (2014) *Omega 3 fatty acids and autism* [online]. Available at: www.researchautism.net/omega-3-fatty-acid-supplements-and-autism (accessed January 13, 2015).

25. NHS Choices (2013) *Fish and Shellfish*. London, UK: NHS.

26. NHS Choices (2011) *Supplements: Who needs them?* London, UK: NHS.

27. Office of Dietary Supplements (2012) *Oral Probiotics: An introduction*. Bethesda, MD: Office of Dietary Supplements.

28. Critchfield JW, van Hemert S, Ash M, Mulder L & Ashwood P (2011) The potential role of probiotics in the management of childhood autism spectrum disorders. *Gastroenterology Research and Practice* **16** 1358.

29. The British Dietetic Association (2012) *Probiotics and Diet.* Birmingham, UK: The British Dietetic Association.

30. Research Autism (2014) *Probiotics, prebiotics and autism* [online]. Available at: www.researchautism.net/probiotics-and-prebiotics (accessed January 13, 2015).

31. Nye C & Brice A (2005) Combined vitamin B-6-magnesium treatment in autism spectrum disorder. *Cochrane Database of Systematic Reviews* CD003497.

32. Research Autism (2014) *Vitamin B-6, magnesium and autism.* [online]. Available at: www.researchautism.net/vitamin-b6-and-autism (accessed January 13, 2015).

33. NHS Choices (2012) *Vitamins and Minerals: B vitamins and folic acid*. London, UK: NHS.

Chapter 20:
Alternative medical procedures

Introduction

We define alternative medical procedures as any medical activities or processes which are used in an alternative or 'off-label' way to treat some of the problems faced by people on the autism spectrum.

For example, some people are using cell therapy, chelation and hyperbaric therapy to tackle a variety of metabolic problems which they think may be the cause of some of the features of autism (such as impaired communication and social difficulties) and related issues (such as challenging behaviours) (1, 2, 3).

Evidence

Some individuals on the autism spectrum may have one or more nutritional and metabolic problems according to a limited amount of research evidence of sufficiently high quality. However, how many individuals on the autism spectrum have these problems is unclear. It is also unclear if these problems cause or worsen the features of autism and related issues, if they arise because of the autism, or if they are completely unrelated to the autism (4).

Most medical procedures currently have very little high-quality research evidence supporting them when they are used as alternative or 'off-label' treatments for people on the autism spectrum (1, 2).

Some medical procedures (such as hyperbaric therapy) are not effective interventions for the treatment of people on the autism spectrum according to a very limited amount of research evidence of sufficiently high quality (3).

Some off-label medical procedures such as chelation may pose significant health risks to some individuals on the autism spectrum (5).

NICE guidelines

The National Institute for Health and Care Excellence generally doesn't support medical procedures for the treatment of autism when used in an alternative or off-label way (6, 7). For example, it recommended that chelation and hyperbaric therapy should not be used.

Supply, quality and regulation

The supply and availability of different medical procedures varies enormously between different procedures, between different countries and even within the same country. For example, procedures which rely on expensive medical equipment (such as hyperbaric oxygen therapy) are less likely to be available in developing countries.

The quality of medical procedures varies enormously depending on the individual practitioner, the type of medical procedure and how it is implemented.

There are some international bodies associated with some types of medical procedure but these bodies generally have no regulatory powers. For example, according to the International Society for Stem Cell Research:

'Cell transplantation is a relatively new technology and the appropriate laws and regulations may not have been developed or applied to the field. Laws and regulations vary from country to country. Depending on the country and the nature of the procedure, there may be no laws restricting stem cell treatments, making them simply unregulated.' (8)

Costs and time

Costs: the cost of using the different types of medical procedures varies enormously between different procedures, between different countries and between different suppliers. For example, taking a chelating agent (usually a pill or a supplement) is likely to be less expensive than using a hyperbaric oxygen chamber (especially if there are additional costs such as overseas travel and accommodation).

Time: the time required to undertake different medical procedures varies enormously between the different procedures. For example, taking a chelating agent may only take a few minutes each day whereas undertaking hyperbaric therapy may require one or more consultations with a specialist, numerous 'dives' in the chamber over several weeks or months, travel to the centre, overnight stays and so on.

Risks and safety

Most medical procedures carry some risk and this risk is likely to be higher when that procedure is used in an off-label way to treat people on the autism spectrum, mainly because of the lack of regulation and agreed protocols.

Specific medical procedures

Cell therapy

Introduction

Cell therapy (also known as cellular therapy or stem cell therapy) includes a variety of procedures in which processed tissue from animal embryos, fetuses, or organs is injected into the body or swallowed.

The processed tissue is designed to replace or regulate the existing cells in the body.

Cell therapy is being used to treat a range of diseases, conditions, and disabilities including Parkinson's disease, motor neurone disease, spinal cord injury, burns, heart disease, diabetes, and arthritis (9, 10).

Cell therapy

Definition: procedures in which processed tissue is injected or swallowed.

Aims: to regulate cells in the bodies of people with autism.

Who: people with autism of any age and any level of ability.

Evidence: insufficient evidence to determine if cell therapy has any benefits.

Risks: pain and discomfort and possibly death.

Aims

Some people think that cell therapy can provide various benefits to people on the autism spectrum by helping to regulate the cells in their bodies.

They think that cells could be designed to target specific functions within the body of people on the autism spectrum, including abnormal neurotransmitter regulation, activated microglia, mitochondrial dysfunction, blood-brain barrier disruptions, and chronic intestinal inflammation (11).

Evidence

Determining the benefits of cell therapy for individuals on the autism spectrum is not currently possible. We must wait for further research of sufficiently high quality to be completed (1).

Risks

The use of cell therapy can be painful, distressing and potentially hazardous depending on how it is administered.

We have seen reports which suggest that cell therapy can lead to significant damage, including death, in some individuals (12).

NICE

The National Institute for Health and Care Excellence has not commented on the use of cell therapy, probably because it is a relatively recent and unproven therapy.

Chelation

Introduction

Chelation (also known as detoxification or detox, pronounced key-LAY-shun) is a medical procedure used to remove toxic substances (such as heavy metals like mercury or lead) from the body.

Chelation involves using one or more 'chelators' – chemicals such as DMSA, DMPS, EDTA, or N-acetylcysteine – to remove the toxic substances from the body (13, 14).

Aims

Some people think that the symptoms of autism and/or related problems (such as challenging behaviours) are caused by or worsened by toxic substances.

They also think that those symptoms can be reduced through the use of chelation.

They think that chelation may be of use to anyone on the autism spectrum who has abnormal levels of heavy metals in their bodies (13, 14).

Chelation

Definition: procedure which removes toxic substances from the body.

Aims: to remove heavy metals from the body.

Who: mainly children with autism, but could be used in people with autism of all ages and all levels of ability.

Evidence: insufficient research evidence to determine if chelation has any benefits.

Risks: serious risks to health, including death.

Evidence

Determining the benefits of chelation for individuals on the autism spectrum is not currently possible. We must wait for further research of sufficiently high quality to be completed (2).

Risks

There are numerous risks associated with chelation. According to one review, 'The chemical substances utilised in chelation treatment have a myriad of potential and potentially serious, side effects, including fever, vomiting, diarrhea, loss of appetite, hypertension, hemorrhoid symptoms, metallic taste, hypotension, cardiac arrhythmias, hypocalcemia, the latter of which can in turn cause fatal cardiac arrest. In 2005, for example, a five-year-old boy with ASD died from cardiac arrest caused by hypocalcemia while receiving intravenous chelation. The potential safety risks associated with chelation recently resulted in a suspension of a clinical study of chelation treatment for autism. Additional safety issues arose from a rodent study that found lasting cognitive impairment' (13).

Additional information

The National Institute for Health and Care Excellence advised:

'Do not use [chelation] to manage autism in any context in children and young people' (6).

Hyperbaric therapy

Introduction

Hyperbaric therapy is the medical use of oxygen at higher-than-atmospheric pressure.

The oxygen is administered to the individual in a pressurised chamber, with the goal of increasing oxygen absorption in bodily tissue.

It is normally used for the treatment of conditions such as embolisms, decompression sickness or carbon monoxide poisoning (16).

Aims

Some people think that individuals on the autism spectrum suffer from a range of metabolic problems, such as oxidative stress – physiological stress on the body caused by the cumulative damage done by free radicals inadequately neutralised by antioxidants.

They think that this may cause many of the problems found in people on the autism spectrum, such as poor eye contact, poor socialisation and lack of attention.

They think that hyperbaric therapy can be used to reduce oxidative stress, leading to a reduction in those behavioural problems (17).

Evidence

Hyperbaric therapy does not provide any benefits to individuals on the autism spectrum according to a very limited amount of research evidence of sufficiently high quality (3).

Hyperbaric therapy

Definition: the medical use of oxygen at higher-than-atmospheric pressure.

Aims: to reduce oxidative stress in people with autism.

Who: people with autism of all ages and levels of ability.

Evidence: very limited amount of research evidence that hyperbaric therapy has no benefits.

Risks: some risks due to the pressure inside the chamber.

Risks

According to Health Canada (2005):

'When used to treat recognised medical conditions, hyperbaric oxygen therapy is generally safe, as long as:

- the chamber is properly installed according to municipal and provincial regulations;
- operators and attendants are properly trained; and
- a certified hyperbaric physician is either on site, or can be reached easily and quickly.

'However, there are risks. Before consenting to treatment, you should consider these factors:

- Pressure inside the chamber can damage the middle and inner ear, nasal sinuses, lungs and teeth in both adults and children.
- Some people experience claustrophobia inside the chamber.

- The therapy may affect your eyes, for example by promoting nearsightedness or cataract growth.
- Because hyperbaric oxygen therapy affects blood-sugar levels, diabetics should have their levels checked before and after treatment.
- A high concentration of oxygen can cause serious complications in some children who have congenital heart disease.
- Too much oxygen can sometimes, although rarely, lead to overload that can cause seizures and lung problems. This is usually prevented by having the patient take breaks to breathe normal air instead of pure oxygen. High concentrations of oxygen at elevated pressures can pose a risk of fire.' (19)

Additional information

The National Institute for Health and Care Excellence recommended:

'Do not use [hyperbaric therapy] to manage autism in any context in children and young people' (6).

Further information

In this book: Please see How to use this book (page 11), Chapter 3 (page 38) for information about interventions, Chapter 4 (page 43) for information about how scientists evaluate those interventions, and Section 3 (page 284) for advice on making the decision about whether or not to use a specific intervention.

Website: Please see www.researchautism.net/alternative-medical-procedures for information about alternative medical procedures including information about specific interventions and details of scientific studies and trials.

References

1. Research Autism (2014) *Cell therapy and autism* [online]. Available at: www.researchautism.net/cell-therapy-and-autism (accessed January 13, 2015).

2. Research Autism (2014) *Chelation and autism* [online]. Available at:www.researchautism.net/chelation-and-autism (accessed January 13, 2015).

3. Research Autism (2014) *Hyperbaric therapy and autism* [online]. Available at: www.researchautism.net/hyperbaric-therapy-and-autism (accessed January 13, 2015).

4. IAN Network (2010) *Mitochondrial Disease and Autism*. Baltimore, MD: IAN Network.

5. Baxter AJ & Krenzelok EP (2008) Pediatric fatality secondary to EDTA chelation. *Clinical Toxicology* **46** 1083–1084.

6. National Institute for Health and Care Excellence (2013) *The Management and Support of Children and Young People on the Autism Spectrum*. London: National Institute for Health and Care Excellence.

7. National Institute for Health and Care Excellence (2012) *Autism: Recognition, referral, diagnosis and management of adults on the autism spectrum*. London: National Institute for Health and Care Excellence.

8. International Society for Stem Cell Research (2014) *Answers to Frequently Asked Questions About Stem Cell Treatments*. Skokie, IL: International Society for Stem Cell Research.

9. National Institutes of Health (2009) *Stem Cell Basics*. Bethesda, MD: National Institutes of Health.

10. International Society for Stem Cell Research (2014) *Top Ten Things to Know About Stem Cell Treatments*. Skokie, IL: International Society for Stem Cell Research.

11. Siniscalco D, Bradstreet JJ, Sych N & Antonucci N (2013) Perspectives on the use of stem cells for autism treatment. *Stem Cells International* **26** 2438.

12. Cyranoski D (2010) Korean deaths spark inquiry. *Nature* 468-485.

13. Davis TN, O'Reilly M, Kang S, Lang R, Rispoli M, Sigafoos J, Lancioni G, Copeland D, Attai S & Mulloy A (2013) Chelation treatment for autism spectrum disorders: a systematic review. *Research in Autism Spectrum Disorders* **7** 49–55.

14. Brent J (2013) Commentary on the abuse of metal chelation therapy in patients with autism spectrum disorders. *Journal of Medical Toxicology*: Official *Journal of the American College of Medical Toxicology* **9** 370–372.

15. American College of Medical Toxicology (2009) *American College of Medical Toxicology Position Statement on Post-Chelator Challenge Urinary Metal Testing*. Phoenix, AZ: Americal College of Medical Toxicology.

16. Ghanizadeh A (2012) Hyperbaric oxygen therapy for treatment of children with autism: a systematic review of randomized trials. *Medical Gas Research* **2** 13.

17. Rossignol DA, Bradstreet JJ, Van Dyke K, Schneider C, Freedenfeld SH, O'Hara N, Cave S, Buckley JA, Mumper EA & Frye RE (2012) Hyperbaric oxygen treatment in autism spectrum disorders. *Medical Gas Research* **2** 16.

18. Kot J & Mathieu D (2011) Controversial issues in hyperbaric oxygen therapy: a European committe for hyperbaric medicine workshop. *Diving and Hyperbaric Medicine* **41** 101–104.

19. Health Canada (2005) *Hyperbaric Oxygen Therapy*. Ottowa, ON: Health Canada.

Chapter 21:
Motor-sensory interventions

Introduction

'Motor interventions' mean any treatments and therapies which use, or which aim to improve, motor functioning (control, co-ordination and movement of the whole body or parts of the body). 'Sensory interventions' mean any treatments and therapies which use, or which aim to improve sensitivity to, one or more of the senses.

Motor-sensory interventions can come in a number of forms, such as combined multi-component therapies (occupational therapy, physiotherapy, sensory integrative therapy), physical activities (martial arts, sports such as running and jogging, yoga), and manipulation interventions (acupuncture, massage, osteopathy).

Some motor-sensory interventions target specific issues such as hearing (auditory integration training), sight (vision therapy), smell and taste (aromatherapy). Other interventions (such as sensory integrative therapy) may be designed to improve a range of motor and sensory functions (1).

Evidence

High-quality evidence shows that some people with autism have sensory issues or motor problems or both (2, 3).

The evidence for motor-sensory interventions is mixed. Auditory integration training does not provide any benefits for people on the autism spectrum according to very limited research evidence of sufficiently high quality (4). Determining the benefits of any other motor-sensory interventions for people on the autism spectrum is not currently possible. We must wait for further research of sufficiently high quality to be completed.

NICE guidelines

The National Institute for Health and Care Excellence did not make any recommendations about most types of motor-sensory interventions. However NICE did recommend (5):

'Do not use auditory integration training to manage speech and language problems in children and young people with autism.'

Supply, quality and regulation

You can undertake some motor-sensory interventions (physical activities such as running, martial arts and yoga) by yourself. You can also purchase the materials for certain motor-sensory interventions (such as weighted blankets or vests) directly from suppliers. Some motor-sensory interventions (such as acupuncture) can only be obtained from a professional.

However, we recommend that you always consult an appropriate professional (such as an occupational therapist or physiotherapist) before trying any kind of motor-sensory intervention. The professional can carry out a proper assessment of your needs, advise you how to get the best from the intervention and also minimise any potential risks.

There are some nationally recognised regulating bodies for some interventions (such as occupational therapy and physiotherapy) but none for other interventions (such as auditory integration training).

Costs and time

Costs: the costs of the different forms of motor-sensory interventions will depend largely on the programme used. For example, the major cost of some interventions (such as weighted blankets) is the cost of the materials and equipment (approximately £100 for a blanket). The major cost of training interventions (such as auditory integration training) is the cost of the assessment and the training (which may be as much as £2,500), plus any associated costs such as travel (6, 7).

Time: the time required will vary depending on the programme used and may also depend on the needs of the individual. For example, auditory integration training is normally delivered over 10 days, 30-minute sessions twice a day, with a minimum of a three-hour rest period between sessions (7). A weighted blanket, on the other hand, may be used every night for many years.

Risks and safety

Some risks are involved in some forms of motor-sensory intervention. For example, any intervention involving movement carries some risk of physical injury, however minor. Risks also come from using specialist equipment (such as some of the machines used in auditory integration training) or specialist materials (such as weighted vests and blankets) (8, 9).

Specific forms of motor-sensory intervention

Auditory integration training

Introduction

Auditory integration training (AIT) involves a person listening to a selection of electronically modified music. Kinds of AIT include the Berard method, the Listening Program, Samonas Sound Therapy, and the Tomatis Method.

AIT is based on the idea that some people are over-sensitive (hypersensitive) or under-sensitive (hyposensitive) to certain frequencies of sound. This sensitivity to certain frequencies is believed to cause a variety of perceptual problems, such as an inability to concentrate or to understand other people. It may also cause other problems such as irritability or lethargy. AIT is designed to improve the person's ability to process sounds by 're-educating' the brain. Playing electronically modified music in which the frequencies have been changed tries to do this (10, 11).

Aims

AIT is often used on children and adults with autism who have additional sensory problems such as painful or hypersensitive hearing.

The aim of AIT is to improve abnormal sound sensitivity in individuals with behavioural disorders including autism.

The supporters of AIT claim that it can lead to better concentration, awareness and a decrease in sound sensitivity. Some go further and claim that it can lead to recovery from autism (12).

Evidence

AIT does not provide any benefits for individuals on the autism spectrum according to a very limited amount of research evidence of sufficiently high quality (4).

Risks

Some individuals may be distressed by the experience of having AIT and damage to hearing due to the volume has been reported. The equipment used, the Audiokinetron, was disallowed for import by the US Food and Drug Administration because of concerns about safety (8).

Auditory integration training

Definition: an intervention where a person listens to a selection of electronically modified music.

Aims: to improve abnormal sound sensitivity.

Who: children and adults with autism who have additional sensory problems such as painful or hypersensitive hearing.

Evidence: very limited amount of research evidence that auditory integration therapy does not provide any benefits.

Risks: some individuals may be distressed by the experience of having AIT and there are some reports of damage to hearing due to volume and sound pressure.

Additional information

The National Institute for Health and Care Excellence reported (5):

'Do not use auditory integration training to manage speech and language problems in children and young people with autism.'

Sensory integrative therapy

Introduction

Sensory integrative therapy is designed to help people cope with sensory difficulties. It is based on the idea that some people struggle to receive, process and make sense of information provided by the senses. The therapist assesses the person's sensory difficulties and then develops a personalised treatment programme using various techniques and tools. A sensory integrative programme usually includes elements such as wearing a weighted vest, being brushed or rubbed by various instruments, sitting on a bouncy ball, and other similar activities (13, 14).

> ### Sensory integrative therapy
>
> **Definition:** an intervention which uses a range of personalised sensory treatments to overcome sensory difficulties.
>
> **Aims:** to help people cope with sensory difficulties.
>
> **Who:** anyone who suffers from sensory over-sensitivity, sensory under-sensitivity, sensory processing disorder, or sensory integration dysfunction.
>
> **Evidence:** insufficient research evidence to determine if sensory integrative therapy has any benefits.
>
> **Risks:** none.

Aims

Sensory integrative therapy is usually for people on the autism spectrum who have sensory over-sensitivity, sensory under-sensitivity, sensory processing disorder or sensory integration dysfunction.

The aim of the therapy is to provide a range of enhanced sensory experiences tailored to the needs of the individual. This is supposed to help them respond better to other sensory experiences, such as loud noises and bright lights.

The supporters of sensory integrative therapy claim that it can remove the problems caused by sensory processing problems. Some of them also claim that it can lead to improvements in other areas, such as social interaction (13, 14).

Evidence

Determining the benefits of sensory integrative therapy for individuals on the autism spectrum is not currently possible. We must wait for further research of sufficiently high quality to be completed (15).

Risks

No risks are associated with sensory integrative therapy, although it is possible that someone could injure themselves when undertaking movement activities such as swinging or trampolining.

Weighted items

Introduction

Weighted items, such as blankets or vests, can be bought from specialist suppliers, bought second-hand or made at home. They are made heavier by adding small weights, which can either be stitched into the fabric or put into specially designed pockets.

The idea behind weighted items is that some children with sensory processing disorders have difficulties with the body's awareness system (proprioception). When this sense does not work properly these children may struggle to understand where they are in space or how they are moving.

Weighted items are designed to regulate proprioception by providing feedback in the form of constant and deep pressure.

Choosing Autism Interventions: A Research-Based Guide © Research Autism and Autism West Midlands

Weighted vests are normally worn for 20–30 minutes at a time during the day, while weighted blankets are used throughout the night (3, 6).

Aims

Weighted items are used by people with autism of any age and any level of ability.

The aim of the therapy is to provide constant and deep pressure to help regulate the body's awareness sense.

The supporters claim that weighted items can lead to a range of improvements including improvements in cognitive functioning, hyperactivity, motor skills, aggressive and self-injurious behaviour and sleep problems (16).

Weighted items

Definition: weighted items include blankets and vests which have been made heavier by adding small weights to them.

Aims: to provide constant and deep pressure to tackle problems such as poor motor skills, hyperactivity and sleeplessness.

Who: people with autism of any age and level of ability.

Evidence: insufficient evidence to determine if weighted items have any benefits.

Risks: when used inappropriately, weighted items can harm the user.

Evidence

Determining the benefits of weighted items for individuals on the autism spectrum is not currently possible. We must wait for further research of sufficiently high quality to be completed (17).

Risks

We know of one case of death due to the use of a weighted blanket. Care should be taken when using weighted items. In particular, the following guidelines have been recommended (9):

- a health professional's advice must be obtained to ensure that the use of the blanket is suitable for the child

- the weight of the blanket must be in proportion of the child's physique and weight
- the child's head must never be, or be able to be, covered by the blanket
- vital signs should always be observable
- the child must never be rolled in a blanket (unless a therapist is constantly at his or her side)
- a child must never be left unsupervised
- the child must be able to easily slip out of the blanket if he or she wishes to do so (it is not a confinement)
- the child must express his or her consent to this, even if it is not verbal.

Further information

In this book: Please see How to use this book (page 11), Chapter 3 (page 38) for information about interventions, Chapter 4 (page 43) for information about how scientists evaluate those interventions, and Section 3 (page 284) for advice on making the decision about whether or not to use a specific intervention.

Websites: Please see www.researchautism.net/motor-sensory-interventions for information about motor sensory interventions including information about specific interventions and details of scientific studies and trials.

References

1. Research Autism (2014) Motor sensory interventions for autism [online]. Available at: www.researchautism.net/motor-sensory-interventions (accessed February 2015).

2. American Psychiatric Association (2013) *Diagnostic and Statistical Manual of Mental Disorders – DSM-5*. Washington, D.C: American Psychiatric Association.

3. Whyatt C & Craig C (2013) Sensory-motor problems in autism. *Frontiers in Integrative Neuroscience* **7** 51.

4. Research Autism (2014) *Auditory integration training and autism* [online]. Available at: www.researchautism.net/auditory-integration-training-and-autism (accessed January 13, 2015).

5. National Institute for Health and Care Excellence (2013) *The Management and Support of Children and Young People on the Autism Spectrum*. London: National Institute for Health and Care Excellence.

6. Gringras P, Green D, Wright B, Rush C, Sparrowhawk M, Pratt K, Allgar V, Hooke N, Moore D, Zaiwalla Z & Wiggs L (2014) Weighted blankets and sleep in autistic children – a randomized controlled trial. *Pediatrics* **134** (2) 298–306.

7. National Light and Sound Therapy Centre (2014) More information about AIT PLUS. Available at: www.light-and-sound.co.uk/autism/AIT_ infosheet.htm (accessed 20 January, 2015).

8. Sinha Y, Silove N, Wheeler D & Williams K (2011) Auditory integration training and other sound therapies for autism spectrum disorders: a systematic review. *Cochrane Database of Systematic Reviews* **7**.

9. College of Occupational Therapists (2011) *The Safe Use of Weighted Blankets*. Private file online.

10. IAN Network (2007) *Sensory Based Therapies*. Baltimore, MD: IAN Network.

11. Brockett SS, Lawton-Shirley NK & Kimball JG (2014) Berard auditory integration training: behavior changes related to sensory modulation. *Autism Insights* **6** 1–10.

12. American Speech-Language-Hearing Association (2003) *Auditory Integration Training*. Rockville, MD: American Speech-Language-Hearing Association.

13. Zimmer M & Desch L (2012) Sensory integration therapies for children with developmental and behavioral disorders. *Pediatrics* **129** 1186–1189.

14. Lang R, O'Reilly M, Healy O, Rispoli M, Lydon H, Streusand W, Davis T, Kang S, Sigafoos J, Lancioni G, Didden R & Giesbers S (2012) Sensory integration therapy for autism spectrum disorders: a systematic review. *Research in Autism Spectrum Disorders* **6** 1004–1018.

15. Research Autism (2014) *Sensory integrative therapy and autism* [online]. Available at: www.researchautism.net/sensory-integrative-therapy-and-autism (accessed January 13, 2015).

16. Stephenson J & Carter M (2009) The use of weighted vests with children with autism spectrum disorders and other disabilities. *Journal of Autism and Developmental Disorders* **39** 105–114.

17. Research Autism (2014) Weighted items and autism [online]. Available at:www.researchautism.net/weighted-items-and-autism (accessed January 13, 2015).

Chapter 22:
Psychological interventions

Introduction

Psychology is the scientific study of the human mind and behaviour: how we think, feel, act and interact, individually and in groups.

Psychology is concerned with all aspects of behaviour and with the thoughts, feelings and motivations underlying that behaviour.

In this chapter, we focus on psychological interventions not covered elsewhere in this book – such as counselling, psychotherapy and creative therapies. For details of other psychological interventions, please see Chapter 9 on behavioural and developmental interventions – page 105.

The psychological therapies described in this chapter are based on the idea that the practitioner can help the person on the autism spectrum to understand (and sometimes change) how they think, feel, and act.

Some people think that some psychological therapies can help people on the autism spectrum who have psychological problems, such as anxiety or depression. Other people think that some psychological therapies can be used to treat the core symptoms of autism, such as difficulties with social communication or social interaction (1).

Evidence

Many people on the autism spectrum have high levels of psychological problems such as anxiety and depression, as shown by strong research evidence (2).

No research evidence shows that any of the core features of autism are caused by underlying psychological issues. However, some research suggests that, when some individuals on the autism spectrum are stressed, they may appear to behave in a more 'autistic' manner. For example, they may find it harder to communicate or to interact with other people, and they may retreat into restricted patterns of thinking or behaviour (3).

Some psychological interventions (such as cognitive behavioural therapy) may be effective in treating some psychological problems (such as anxiety) in some people on the autism spectrum according to a limited amount of evidence of sufficiently high quality (4). Some creative therapies (such as music therapy) may be effective in improving social and communication skills in some children and adolescents on the autism spectrum according to an extremely limited amount of evidence of sufficiently high quality (5). Determining if other psychological therapies (such as mindfulness training) provide any benefits to individuals on the autism spectrum is not possible until further research of sufficiently high quality has been completed (6).

NICE guidelines

The National Institute for Health and Care Excellence did not make any recommendations about most of the psychological therapies described in this chapter. However, it did recommend that adults with autism and co-existing mental disorders should be offered psychosocial interventions (such as CBT) informed by existing NICE guidance for the specific disorder. It also recommended that those interventions should be adapted to meet the needs of individuals with autism. This might include, for example, using 'a more concrete and structured approach with a greater use of written and visual information (which may include worksheets, thought bubbles, images and 'tool boxes')' and 'placing greater emphasis on changing behaviour, rather than cognitions, and using the behaviour as the starting point for intervention' (7).

Supply, quality and regulation

Psychological therapies may be given by psychologists (someone who has trained in psychology), psychiatrists (medical doctors who have qualified in psychiatry) or psychotherapists (who may be psychiatrists, psychologists or other mental health professionals who have trained in psychotherapy) (8).

There are a number of organisations which regulate some providers of psychological therapies. Most reputable counsellors will be registered with a professional organisation that has been accredited by the Professional Standards Authority, such as the British Association for Counselling and Psychotherapy or The National Counselling Society. Counselling and clinical psychologists must be registered with the Health and Care Professions Council and may also be chartered with The British Psychological Society (9).

The title 'psychotherapist' is not restricted. So anyone can call themselves a psychotherapist. But to be recognised by the NHS or by many private insurers psychotherapists have to have a psychotherapy qualification, typically requiring four years of postgraduate study, supervised practice, and some element of personal therapy or learning about themselves. Some psychotherapists are regulated by organisations such as the British Association of Counselling and Psychotherapy or the United Kingdom Council for Psychotherapy (10, 11).

However, as most psychological therapies are not designed specifically for autism, this does not necessarily mean that the therapist will be competent to work complex cases such as with individuals on the autism spectrum.

Costs and time

Costs: the costs of different psychological therapies will depend on the charges of individual therapists but can range from £10–70 per hour or sometimes more. Some psychological therapies (such as CBT, counselling and music therapy) are available on the NHS in some areas.

Time: typical psychological therapies involve regular sessions, which can range in frequency from twice a week, to monthly. Counselling and psychotherapy may continue for many years, with the agreement of the client and the counsellor. Most counsellors and psychotherapists will suggest initially that a much shorter number of sessions are planned (from four to 12) and if the client wishes to continue an agreement is made for another block of meetings.

Choosing Autism Interventions: A Research-Based Guide © Research Autism and Autism West Midlands

The length of sessions will usually vary from 30 minutes to an hour and a half (for group and family therapy). Counselling and psychotherapy is usually weekly, and may last for 50 minutes or so.

Risks and safety

All psychological therapies pose some risks. For example, according to the Royal College of Psychiatrists:

'All effective treatments carry some risk. During psychotherapy there may be spells of being in touch with painful emotions, sometimes for the first time, which may temporarily lead to feeling worse. This is part of the process of facing, and learning to live with, one's feelings.'

'Risks are minimised by skilful assessment of suitability for psychotherapy and by the availability of experienced and properly qualified psychotherapists.' (12)

Specific forms of psychological therapy

Counselling

Introduction

Counselling is a type of talking therapy that allows a person to talk about their problems and feelings in a relaxed, stress-free and confidential environment.

A counsellor is trained to listen with empathy (by putting themselves in your shoes). They can help you deal with any negative thoughts and feelings that you have.

Counselling is based on the idea that talking about a problem may help to understand and to solve that problem.

Sometimes you may also be encouraged to discuss problems with other people, in couple therapy, family therapy or group therapy (9).

Aims

Counselling is mainly used with older children and adults with autism who are higher-functioning (with an IQ of 70 or above).

Counselling is used to tackle a range of problems facing people on the autism spectrum including mental health problems (such as anxiety and depression) or relationship difficulties (such as making friends or getting angry with other people).

Some people claim that counselling can be a useful method to deal with many of the problems facing people on the autism spectrum (13).

Evidence

Determining the benefits of counselling for individuals on the autism spectrum is not currently possible. We must wait for further research of sufficiently high quality to be completed (14).

Risks

No risks are associated with counselling other than those found in other psychological therapies.

Additional information

Counselling and psychotherapy are very closely related, with their differences being mainly historical. They differ from other psychological therapies in placing great emphasis on the quality of the relationship between the counsellor or psychotherapist, since there is good, high quality evidence that the quality of this relationship determines to a large degree whether or not the client benefits from counselling or psychotherapy.

Psychotherapy

Introduction

Psychotherapy is a type of therapy used to treat emotional problems and mental health conditions.

It involves talking to a trained therapist, either one-to-one, in a group or with your wife, husband or partner. It allows you to look deeper into your problems and worries and deal with troublesome habits and a wide range of mental disorders, such as depression and schizophrenia.

Psychotherapy usually involves talking but sometimes other methods may be used – for example, art, music, drama and movement.

Psychotherapy can help you to discuss feelings you have about yourself and other people, particularly family and those close to you. In some cases, couples or families are offered joint therapy sessions together (15).

Aims

Different types of psychotherapy may be used for different groups of individuals on the autism spectrum. For example, CBT is mainly used with older children and adults with autism who are higher-functioning (with an IQ of 70 or above) whereas music therapy can be used with individuals of any age and ability (4, 5).

Psychotherapy is used to tackle a range of problems facing people on the autism spectrum including mental health problems (such as anxiety and depression) or relationship difficulties (such as making friends or getting angry with other people).

Some people claim that some forms of psychotherapy can be a useful method to deal with many of the problems facing people on the autism spectrum (16).

Evidence

Determining the benefits of psychotherapy for individuals on the autism spectrum is difficult because it includes such a wide range of practices, each of which has different levels of research evidence (17).

Risks

No risks are associated with psychotherapy other than those found in other psychological therapies.

Cognitive behavioural therapy

Introduction

Cognitive behavioural therapy (CBT) is designed to help people identify their thoughts and feelings and change the thoughts that are unhelpful. It is used to treat a number of psychological issues including anxiety and anger. It is based on the idea that how we think, how we feel and how we act can affect each other. For example, a person who thinks that an increased heart rate is the sign of a heart attack is more likely to panic than a person who thinks that it is just a normal variation in heart rate (17).

CBT uses a variety of techniques to help people become more aware of how they think, so that they can change how they think and therefore how they behave. For example, some forms of CBT include keeping a diary to record feelings and behaviours (18, 19).

> **Cognitive behavioural therapy**
>
> **Definition:** a psychological therapy which is designed to help the person identify what they are feeling and thinking and change the thoughts which are unhelpful.
>
> **Aims:** to treat anxiety and other mental health problems in people with autism.
>
> **Who:** high-functioning individuals over the age of eight.
>
> **Evidence:** limited amount of research evidence that CBT may provide some benefits for anxiety in people with autism.
>
> **Risks:** discussing painful emotions may be difficult.

Aims

Cognitive behavioural therapy is mainly used with older children (eight and above) and adults with autism who are higher

functioning (with an IQ or 70 or above) because it requi
to monitor and manage their own thoughts and behavio

CBT is commonly used to tackle a range of mental healt
problems such as anxiety and anger. Some people think
by helping a person with autism change how they think about
a situation and giving them some coping strategies they will be
able to reduce those problems.

Some people also think that CBT can be used to target the core
symptoms of autism, such as difficulties with social interaction
and communication (18, 19, 20).

Evidence

Some CBT programmes may help some high-functioning
individuals on the autism spectrum over the age of eight deal
with anxiety – provided those programmes have been modified to
meet the needs of individuals with autism – according to a limited
amount of research evidence of sufficiently high quality (4).

Risks

We have not identified any risks associated with CBT other than
those found in other psychological therapies.

Additional information

A number of criticisms about the use of CBT in people with autism
have been made, and these all centre on whether CBT is a suitable
intervention for people with autism. Please visit the Research
Autism website for a more detailed overview of the criticisms (4).

Creative and expressive therapies

Introduction

Creative and expressive therapies are a form of psychological
therapy where a therapist uses a creative or expressive art form
to help a client. They are based on the idea that all individuals
can respond to creative and expressive activities and that this

can lead to positive changes in behaviour and emotional well-being. The client does not need creative or expressive skills to benefit from these therapies but the therapist does need a high level of therapeutic skill. Creative and expressive therapies include music therapy, drama therapy, art therapy and dance movement therapy (21, 22).

Aims

Creative and expressive therapies are designed to be used by people with autism of any age and any level of ability.

Some people claim that creative and expressive therapies can be used to target the core features of autism such as difficulties in social communication and social interaction by increasing self-awareness and awareness of others, building relationships and exercising joint attention. Some people also claim that creative and expressive therapies can be used to help some people with autism deal with sensory issues (for example music therapy) and motor co-ordination (for example dance movement therapy) (21, 22).

Creative and expressive therapies

Definition: any intervention in which a therapist uses a creative or expressive art form to help a client.

Aims: to target the core features of autism, such as difficulties with social communication and social interaction.

Who: people of any age and level of ability.

Evidence: insufficient evidence to determine if art therapy and dramatherapy have any benefits. Extremely limited amount of research evidence that music therapy may provide some benefits.

Risks: discussing painful emotions may be difficult.

Evidence

Music therapy may provide some benefits for some individuals on the autism spectrum according to an extremely limited amount of research evidence of a sufficiently high quality (5).

Determining the benefits of other creative therapies for individuals on the autism spectrum is not currently possible. We must wait for further research of sufficiently high quality to be completed.

Risks

No specific risks are associated with creative and expressive therapies other than those found in other psychological therapies.

Mindfulness training

Introduction

Mindfulness is a way of thinking about the present moment in a particular way in order to reduce the influence of emotion on a person's response. It focuses on paying attention to the moment in a non-judgmental and accepting way. It is often used to reduce stress, anxiety and depression. It is based on the idea that by analysing a moment in a non-judgmental way, a person can respond to a situation in a much less emotional way and therefore deal with distressing situations better. By training people to examine the present moment in a different way, mindfulness training can help a person to respond differently. Mindfulness training may include meditation, yoga and breathing exercises (23).

Mindfulness training

Definition: an intervention which aims to help a person examine the current moment in a non-judgmental and accepting way.

Aims: to change how a person responds to distressing situations.

Who: parents of children with autism; high-functioning adolescents and adults with autism.

Evidence: insufficient evidence to determine if mindfulness training has any benefits.

Risks: thinking about painful emotions may be difficult.

Aims and claims

Mindfulness training is used in both people with autism (usually higher-functioning adolescents and adults) and parents of children with autism. Some people claim that mindfulness training can reduce anxiety and depression in people on the autism spectrum. Others claim that it can reduce aggressive behaviour in people on the spectrum (23, 24). Some people also claim that mindfulness training can reduce the stress experienced by parents of children on the spectrum.

Evidence

Determining the benefits of mindfulness training for individuals on the autism spectrum and their parents or carers is not currently possible. We must wait for further research of sufficiently high quality to be completed (6).

Risks

No risks are associated with mindfulness training other than those found in other psychological therapies.

Further information

In this book: Please see How to use this book (page 11), Chapter 3 (page 38) for information about interventions, Chapter 4 (page 43) for information about how scientists evaluate those interventions, and Section 3 (page 284) for advice on making the decision about whether or not to use a specific intervention.

Websites: Please see www.researchautism.net/motor-sensory-interventions for information about motor sensory interventions including information about specific interventions and details of scientific studies and trials.

References

1. Research Autism (2014) *Psychological interventions and autism* [online]. Available at: www.researchautism.net/psychological-interventions (accessed January 13, 2015).

2. Lai M-C, Lombardo MV & Baron-Cohen S (2014) Autism. *Lancet* **383** 896–910.

3. White SW, Oswald D, Ollendick T & Scahill L (2009) Anxiety in children and adolescents with autism spectrum disorders. *Clinical Psychology Review* **29** 216–29.

4. Research Autism (2014) *Cognitive behavioural therapy and autism*. [online]. Available at: www.researchautism.net/cognitive-behavioural-therapy-and-autism (accessed January 13, 2015).

5. Research Autism (2014) *Music therapy and autism*. [online]. Available at: www.researchautism.net/music-therapy-and-autism (accessed January 13, 2015).

6. Research Autism (2014) *Mindfulness training and autism*. [online]. Available at: www.researchautism.net/mindfulness-training (accessed January 13, 2015).

7. National Institute for Health and Care Excellence (2012) *Autism: Recognition, referral, diagnosis and management of adults on the autism spectrum*. London: National Institute for Health and Care Excellence.

8. NHS (2013) *Differences Between Psychology, Psychiatry and Psychotherapy*. London, UK: NHS.

9. NHS Choices (2012) *Counselling*. London, UK: NHS.

10. British Association of Counselling and Psychotherapy (2015) *British Association of Counselling and Psychotherapy*. Available at: http://www.bacp.co.uk/ (accessed January 30, 2015).

11. United Kingdom Council for Psychotherapy (2013) *United Kingdom Council for Psychotherapy*. Available at: http://www.psychotherapy.org.uk/ (accessed January 30, 2015).

12. Royal College of Psychiatrists (2015) *FAQs about Psychotherapy*. London, UK: Royal College of Psychiatrists.

13. National Autistic Society (2014) *Counselling*. London: National Autistic Society.

14. Research Autism (2014) *Counselling and autism*. [online]. Available at: www.researchautism.net/counselling (accessed January 13, 2015).

15. NHS (2013) *Psychotherapy*. London, UK: NHS.

16. Bromfield R (2000) It's the tortoise race: long-term psychodynamic psychotherapy with a high-functioning autistic adolescent. *Psychoanalytic Inquiry* **20** (5) 732–745

17. Research Autism (2014) *Psychotherapy and autism*. [online]. Available at: www.researchautism.net/psychotherapy (accessed January 13, 2015).

18. IAN Network (2012) *Cognitive Behavioral Therapies and Autism Spectrum Disorders*. Baltimore, MD: IAN Network.

19. Wood JJ, Fujii C, Renno P & Van Dyke M (2014) Impact of Cognitive Behavioral Therapy on Observed Autism Symptom Severity During School Recess: A Preliminary Randomized, Controlled Trial. *Journal of Autism and Developmental Disorders*.

20. Sukhodolsky DG, Bloch MH, Panza KE & Reichow B (2013) Cognitive-behavioral therapy for anxiety in children with high-functioning autism: a meta-analysis. *Pediatrics* **132** e1341–50.

21. Geretsegger M, Elefant C, Ka M & Gold C (2014) Music therapy for people with autism spectrum disorder. *Cochrane Database of Systematic Reviews* **6** CD00438.

22. Research Autism (2014) *Dance movement therapy and autism* [online]. Available at: www.researchautism.net/dance-movement-therapy (accessed January 13, 2015).

23. Spek A a, van Ham NC & Nyklíček I (2013) Mindfulness-based therapy in adults with an autism spectrum disorder: a randomized controlled trial. *Research in Developmental Disabilities* **34** 246–53.

24. Bluth K, Roberson PNE, Billen RM & Sams JM (2013) A Stress Model for Couples Parenting Children With Autism Spectrum Disorders and the Introduction of a Mindfulness Intervention. *Journal of Family Theory & Review* **5** 194–213.

Chapter 23:
Social care services

Introduction

Social care services are based in the community and are designed for assessing the needs of, and providing support to, people with any social needs due to mental or physical disabilities.

Residential care, supported living schemes, social groups, and respite care are among the many different kinds of social care service for autism (1).

Social care services are provided on the basis that some people on the autism spectrum and their families are unable to obtain all of the support that they need by themselves.

Evidence

Some people on the autism spectrum need some support that their families may not be able to provide, according to high-quality research evidence. Some families may also need some forms of support, according to high-quality research evidence (2).

Determining the benefits of most social care services for individuals on the autism spectrum is not currently possible. We must wait for further research of sufficiently high quality to be completed.

NICE guidelines

The National Institute for Health and Care Excellence has made recommendations about various social care services, although it did not comment on their effectiveness. For example, NICE made the following recommendations about residential care and supported living (3, 4):

'If residential care is needed for adults with autism it should usually be provided in small, local community-based units (of no more than six people and with well-supported single person accommodation). The environment should be structured to support and maintain a collaborative approach between the person with autism and their family, partner or carer(s) for the development and maintenance of interpersonal and community living skills.'

It also made recommendations about short breaks and respite care:

'Offer families (including siblings) and carers an assessment of their own needs, including whether they have (…) practical support in their caring role, including short breaks and emergency plans.'

'If the sleep problems continue to impact on the child or young person or their parents or carers, consider (…) short breaks and other respite care for one night or more. Short breaks may need to be repeated regularly to ensure that parents or carers are adequately supported. Agree the frequency of breaks with them and record this in the care plan.'

Supply, quality and regulation

In the UK, social care services may be provided by the local social services or social work department, by a social enterprise or not-for-profit organisation, or by a parent or carer. Some providers of social care services (for example social workers) can get recognised professional qualifications. Many of these services are inspected by the Care Quality Commission and any person providing social care services to children and vulnerable adults should have a Disclosure and Barring Service (DBS) check (1).

Costs and time

Costs: the cost will depend largely on the needs of the individual and the service provided. In many cases funding may be available from government or other agencies to cover some of the costs.

Time: the time will depend largely on the needs of the individual and the type of service provided. Some services, such as short breaks, may only be needed for a short period of time, such as a day or overnight. Others are long-term services, with 24-hour care provided over many years (for example in residential services).

Risks and safety

The majority of social care services are well-run and pose no risks for people on the autism spectrum. However, a number of high-profile cases have shown that some social care services are not well run and may pose very significant risks. The Winterbourne View residential home (in which the residents were emotionally and physically abused by staff) is probably the most notorious (5) and the Slade House assessment and treatment unit (where a young adult with learning disabilities and epilepsy drowned while unattended) was also widely publicised at the time (6).

Specific forms of social care services

Residential care

Introduction

Residential care is a service where a person with autism lives in a home and requires high levels of support. The residential service may be specifically for people with autism or may be targeted for people with learning disabilities and autism or other groups. Some residential care homes involve service users in decision making, support service users in doing things independently and accessing the community, provide a variety of leisure and social environments, and respect people's privacy (7).

Residential care

Definition: a service provided where a person with autism lives in a home and requires high levels of support.

Aims: to provide 24-hour care to people with a high level of need.

Who: older children and adults with autism who have a high level of need.

Evidence: insufficient evidence to determine if residential care provides any benefits.

Risks: some risks including isolation and institutionalisation.

Aims

Residential services are provided to older children and adults of any age and any level of ability who have a high level of need.

The aim of residential care for people with autism is to provide long-term, high levels of care that cannot be provided in other ways.

Some people claim that people with autism can have a good quality of life in smaller, person-centred residential care homes (8).

Evidence

Determining the benefits of residential care for individuals on the autism spectrum is not currently possible. We must wait for further research of sufficiently high quality to be completed (9).

Risks

Some risks are associated with residential care homes for people with autism. For example, there have been cases where a care home has not been available within a person's own community resulting in them being moved to other parts of the country. The Department of Health Winterbourne View Review Concordat states that services should be provided locally (10), but services are not yet available everywhere. Institutionalisation is also a risk, and is defined as 'when the routines, systems and regimes of an institution result in poor or inadequate standards of care and poor practice which affects the whole setting and denies, restricts or curtails the dignity, privacy, choice, independence or fulfilment of adults at risk' (11).

Short breaks

Introduction

Short breaks, also known as respite care, consist of regular, short breaks during which individuals with autism spend some time away from their immediate family. Respite carers help people with autism to enjoy opportunities and take part in activities that they may not otherwise get, such as trips to the seaside. During the break, parents and siblings are given a break from the demands of caring for the person with autism. They get time for themselves and the chance to enjoy their own company (12).

Aims

Short breaks are sometimes offered to the parents, siblings and other carers of people on the autism spectrum.

Short breaks aim to provide the person with autism the opportunity to do things they have never tried before and to give families the chance to have a break from caring for the person with autism.

Some people claim that short breaks can improve the quality of life of people with autism and their families by offering new opportunities for people with autism and giving families the opportunity to rest and recuperate (12).

Short breaks

Definition: short breaks during which people with autism spend some time away from their immediate family, also known as respite care.

Aims: to enjoy opportunities and take part in activities they may not otherwise get, and to provide families with a chance to have a break from caring for the person with autism.

Who: people with autism of all ages and abilities, and their families.

Evidence: insufficient evidence to determine if short breaks have any benefits.

Risks: none.

Evidence

Determining the benefits of short breaks for individuals on the autism spectrum is not currently possible. We must wait for further research of sufficiently high quality to be completed (13).

Risks

Some risks are associated with short breaks. Individuals receiving these services are at risk from of abuse from their care workers and others because they are vulnerable.

Social groups

Introduction

Social groups provide an opportunity for people to meet others with the same or a similar diagnosis and also provide an opportunity for people on the autism spectrum to improve their social skills in a safe, supportive environment.

The groups are usually facilitated by professionals or volunteers but offer flexibility in the leisure activities they provide. For example, some may focus on one activity, such as drama, and others may offer a wider range of activities. Social groups differ from social skills groups (see page 157) in that they are less focused on learning skills and more focused on providing opportunities for people to participate in mainstream leisure (14).

Social groups

Definition: an opportunity for people with autism to meet each other and improve their social skills.

Aims: to improve social skills, build relationships and try new things.

Who: people with autism of any age and level of ability.

Evidence: insufficient evidence to determine if social groups have any benefits.

Risks: none.

Aims

Social groups can be designed for people with autism of any age and any level of ability. The aim of social groups is to provide opportunities for people with autism to meet others, improve their social skills and take part in various activities.

Some people claim that social groups can improve social skills and develop relationships between people with autism (14).

Evidence

Determining the benefits of social groups for individuals on the autism spectrum is not currently possible. We must wait for further research of sufficiently high quality to be completed (15).

Risks

No risks are associated with social groups for people with autism.

Choosing Autism Interventions: A Research-Based Guide © Research Autism and Autism West Midlands

Supported living

Introduction

Supported living is where the person with autism is supported to choose where they live, whether anyone lives with them, and who supports them. The people in supported living are supported to manage their day-to-day lives including having a tenancy agreement, paying their bills and accessing the community. Supported living can be adapted to the individual needs of the person being supported. Some people will still have high levels of need (24-hour care) while others may need one or two hours a day or a few hours a week (16, 17).

Supported living

Definition: a service where people with autism are supported to choose where they live, who lives with them and who supports them.

Aims: to allow people to have a choice in how their lives are run while offering them the support they need.

Who: adults with autism of any age and any level of ability.

Evidence: insufficient evidence to determine if supported living has any benefits.

Risks: none.

Aims

Supported living may be provided for adults with autism of any age and any level of ability.

The aim of supported living services for autism is to support people to have a choice in how they live and run their lives, while still offering them the support they need.

Some people claim that supported living services offer people with autism a chance to live independently and have more access to the community (16, 17).

Evidence

Determining the benefits of supported living for individuals on the autism spectrum is not currently possible. We must wait for further research of sufficiently high quality to be completed (18).

Risks

Some risks are associated with supported living services. Adults with autism receiving these services are at risk from many forms of abuse from their care workers and others because they are vulnerable.

Further information

In this book: Please see How to use this book (page 11), Chapter 3 (page 38) for information about interventions, Chapter 4 (page 43) for information about how scientists evaluate those interventions, and Section 3 (page 284) for advice on making the decision about whether or not to use a specific intervention.

Website: Please see www.researchautism.net/social-care-services for information about different social care services including information about specific services and details of scientific studies and trials.

References

1. NHS Choices (2014) *Guide to Social Care Services*. London, UK: NHS.

2. Barnard J *et al* (2001) *Ignored or ineligible? The reality for adults with autism spectrum disorders*. London: National Autistic Society.

3. National Institute for Health and Care Excellence (2013) *The Management and Support of Children and Young People on the Autism Spectrum*. London: National Institute for Health and Care Excellence.

4. National Institute for Health and Care Excellence (2012) *Autism: Recognition, referral, diagnosis and management of adults on the autism spectrum*. London: National Institute for Health and Care Excellence.

5. Cafe R (2012) Winterbourne View: Abuse footage shocked nation. BBC News. Available at: www.bbc.co.uk/news/uk-england-bristol-20084254 (accessed 16 January, 2015).

6. BBC (2014) Slade House patient Connor Sparrowhawk's death 'preventable'. BBC News. Available at: www.bbc.co.uk/news/uk-england-oxfordshire-26334445 (accessed 16 January, 2015).

7. NHS Choices (2013) *Care Homes*. London, UK: NHS.

8. Alvarez J & Crabtree J (2009) The effects of residential setting on the quality of life of adults with autism spectrum conditions. *Good Autism Practice* **9** 3–8.

9. Research Autism (2014) *Residential care and autism* [online]. Available at:www.researchautism.net/residential-care (accessed January 13, 2015).

10. Department of Health (2012) *Winterbourne View Review: Concordat: A programme of action*. London, UK: Department of Health.

11. Social Care Institute for Excellence (2010) *Institutionalised Care*. London, UK: SCIE.

12. Harper A *et al* (2014) Respite care, marital quality, and stress in parents of children with autism spectrum disorders. *Journal of Autism and Developmental Disorders* **43** (11) 2604–2616.

13. Research Autism (2014) *Short breaks and autism* [online]. Available at: www.researchautism.net/short-breaks (accessed January 13, 2015).

14. National Autistic Society (2014) *Social Skills for Adolescents*. London: National Autistic Society.

15. Research Autism (2014) *Social groups and autism* [online]. Available at: www.researchautism.net/social-groups-and-autism (accessed January 13, 2015).

16. Care Quality Commission (2011) *Supported Living Schemes: Regulated activities for which the provider may need to register*. London, UK: CQC.

17. Sines D, Hogard E & Ellis R (2012) Evaluating quality of life in adults with profound learning difficulties resettled from hospital to supported living in the community. *Journal of Intellectual Disabilities* **16** (4) 247–263.

18. Research Autism (2014) *Supported living and autism* [online]. Available at: www.researchautism.net/supported-living (accessed January 13, 2015).

Chapter 24:
Vocational interventions

Introduction

Vocational interventions are any activities that are designed to help people find, get and keep a job. They also include any activities which enable people to improve the workplace experience and enhance their careers.

Some vocational interventions (such as some supported employment programmes) are specifically designed to help people on the autism spectrum. Some vocational interventions (such as some sheltered employment programmes) are designed to help a variety of disadvantaged adults who may find it difficult to find a job. Other interventions (such as on-the-job coaching) are designed to help anyone in the workplace, irrespective of whether they are disadvantaged or not (1).

Evidence

Determining the benefits of most forms of vocational intervention (such as sheltered employment programmes) for people on the autism spectrum is not currently possible. We must wait for further research of sufficiently high quality to be completed. Some supported employment programmes may provide some benefits for some individuals on the autism spectrum according to an extremely limited amount of research evidence of sufficiently high quality (2).

NICE guidelines

The National Institute for Health and Care Excellence has not made any recommendations on most forms of vocational intervention. However it did recommend (3, 4):

'For adults with autism without a learning disability or with a mild learning disability, who are having difficulty obtaining or maintaining employment, consider an individual supported employment programme.

'Offer children and young people with autism support in developing coping strategies and accessing community services, including developing skills to access public transport, employment and leisure facilities.'

Supply, quality and regulation

Vocational services may be provided by a commercial organisation, a social enterprise or not-for-profit organisation, by an educational establishment (such as a college) or by a parent or carer. Some of these providers have no nationally recognised regulation.

Costs and time

Cost: the cost will depend largely on the needs of the individual and the service provided. In many cases funding may be available from the employing organisation, from the organisation providing the intervention or from the government.

Time: the time will depend largely on the needs of the individual and the type of service provided. Some services (such as on-the-job coaching) may only be needed for a short time, such as over the course of a week. Others are long-term services, with care provided over many years (for example in sheltered employment).

Risks and safety

No risks are associated with vocational interventions.

Specific forms of vocational intervention

Supported employment

Introduction

Supported employment is a service provided to disadvantaged adults looking to find and retain a job. It is based on the idea that, with appropriate help, these people can find and keep a job in the competitive marketplace rather than being unemployed or working in a sheltered workshop. Supported employment programmes usually consist of a range of specific techniques such as:

- job development, including helping someone find appropriate jobs
- job placement, including matching someone to an appropriate job
- job-site training, which involves on-site skills training
- assessment, which is an ongoing process to determine how the worker is performing
- job retention, which involves advocacy and procedures to ensure long-term job maintenance (5).

Aims

Supported employment is designed for adults with autism with no learning disabilities or mild learning disabilities.

The aim of supported employment is to help a person with autism find and keep a job.

Some people claim that supported employment can improve quality of life and independence for people with autism and lead to successful employment in the community (6).

Evidence

Supported employment may provide some benefits for some individuals on the autism spectrum according to an extremely limited amount of research evidence of sufficiently high quality (2).

Risks

No risks are associated with supported employment.

Supported employment

Definition: a service provided to help people with autism to find and keep a job in a competitive environment.

Aims: to help people with autism find and keep a job.

Who: adults with autism with no learning disabilities or mild learning disabilities.

Evidence: extremely limited amount of research evidence that supported employment may provide some benefits.

Risks: none.

Sheltered employment

Introduction

Sheltered employment refers to programmes which are designed to assist individuals who, for whatever reason, are viewed as not capable of working in a competitive employment setting in their local community. Some sheltered employment programmes provide training and services that will assist people to develop life skills as well as educational and pre-vocational skills (7).

Sheltered employment

Definition: a programme designed to assist people who cannot work in competitive employment.

Aim: to offer people with autism the opportunity to work in a sheltered environment.

Who: adults with autism who cannot work in a competitive environment.

Evidence: insufficient evidence to determine if sheltered employment has any benefits.

Risks: none.

Aims

The aim of sheltered employment is to provide people who are not seen as capable of working in a competitive environment with the opportunity to work in a sheltered environment.

Some people claim that sheltered employment can help people develop skills which could prepare them for work in a competitive environment and improve quality of life (7).

Evidence

Determining the benefits of sheltered employment for individuals on the autism spectrum is not currently possible. We must wait for further research of sufficiently high quality to be completed (8).

Risks

No risks are associated with sheltered employment.

Other vocational interventions

Introduction

Other vocational interventions exist to help people in the workplace. These include (9, 10):

- job applications: help in making job applications
- job placement: matching someone to an appropriate job
- job-site training: on-site skills training
- co-workers: training co-workers and bosses so that they understand the needs of the disadvantaged employee
- workplace modifications: adapting the workplace to suit the employee
- technology: various, including use of video modelling to teach vocational skills and iPads as prompts that remind someone to do a task at a set time.

> ## Other vocational interventions
>
> **Definition:** a range of other interventions provided to help people with autism in the workplace.
>
> **Aims:** to help people with autism in the workplace.
>
> **Who:** adults with autism of any ability.
>
> **Evidence:** insufficient evidence to determine if other vocational interventions have any benefits.
>
> **Risks:** none.

Aims

Different vocational interventions may be designed for adults with autism of different abilities. For example, some vocational interventions may not be appropriate for adults with both autism and a learning disability.

The aim will vary from one intervention to another. Some may be designed to improve interview skills, some may be designed to improve work performance, some may be designed to help the employee understand social situations at work.

Some people claim that some of these other vocational interventions can lead to more successful employment (9, 10).

Evidence

Determining the benefits of other vocational interventions for individuals on the autism spectrum is not currently possible. We must wait for further research of sufficiently high quality to be completed.

Risks

No risks are associated with most other vocational interventions.

Further information

In this book: Please see How to use this book (page 11), Chapter 3 (page 38) for information about interventions, Chapter 4 (page 43) for information about how scientists evaluate those interventions, and Section 3 (page 284) for advice on making the decision about whether or not to use a specific intervention.

Website: Please see www.researchautism.net/vocational-interventions for information about different vocational interventions including information about specific interventions and details of scientific studies and trials.

References

1. Taylor JL, McPheeters ML, Sathe NA, Dove D, Veenstra-VanderWeele J & Warren Z (2012) A systematic review of vocational interventions for young adults with autism spectrum disorders. *Pediatrics* **130** 531–538.

2. Research Autism (2014) *Supported employment and autism* [online]. Available at: www.researchautism.net/supported-employment-and-autism (accessed January 13, 2015).

3. National Institute for Health and Care Excellence (2013) *The Management and Support of Children and Young People on the Autism Spectrum*. London: National Institute for Health and Care Excellence.

4. National Institute for Health and Care Excellence (2012) *Autism: Recognition, referral, diagnosis and management of adults on the autism spectrum*. London: National Institute for Health and Care Excellence.

5. British Association for Supported Employment (2014) *What is Supported Employment?* Tottington, UK: British Association for Supported Employment.

6. Wehman PH, Schall CM, McDonough J, Kregel J, Brooke V, Molinelli A, Ham W, Graham CW, Erin Riehle J, Collins HT & Thiss W (2014) Competitive employment for youth with autism spectrum disorders: early results from a randomized clinical trial. *Journal of Autism and Developmental Disorders* **44** 487–500.

7. Cimera RE, Wehman P, West M & Burgess S (2012) Do sheltered workshops enhance employment outcomes for adults with autism spectrum disorder? *Autism:the International Journal of Research and Practice* **16** 87–94.

8. Research Autism (2014) *Sheltered employment and autism* [online]. Available at: www.researchautism.net/sheltered-employment (accessed January 13, 2015).

9. Hendricks DR & Wehman P (2009) Transition from school to adulthood for youth with autism spectrum disorders: review and recommendations. *Focus on Autism and Other Developmental Disabilities* **24** 77–88.

10. Nicholas DB, Attridge M, Zwaigenbaum L & Clarke M (2014) Vocational support approaches in autism spectrum disorder: a synthesis review of the literature. *Autism* **19** (2) 235–245.

Chapter 25:
Animal-assisted activities and therapies

Introduction

Animal-assisted activities are any activities that involve a person interacting with animals in some way. For example, the person with autism may use an assistance dog, swim or touch dolphins, learn to ride and groom a horse, or keep a pet hamster.

Animal-assisted therapies are activities designed to help individuals meet specific therapeutic goals and are usually based around structured encounters with the animals.

Animal-assisted therapies may be designed to achieve a range of aims. For example, they may be designed to reduce fear of specific animals, teach responsibility and commitment, teach problem-solving and decision-making skills, or improve language and social skills. These interventions may be used simply to help facilitate other therapies and interactions with a human therapist (1, 2).

Evidence

Determining the benefits of most animal-assisted activities and therapies for individuals on the autism spectrum is not currently possible. We must wait for further research of sufficiently high quality to be completed. However, there is evidence that some equine-assisted therapies may provide some benefits to some individuals on the autism spectrum according to some extremely limited research evidence of sufficiently high quality (3).

NICE guidelines

No guidance is provided on animal-assisted activities and therapies and autism by the National Institute for Health and Care Excellence (NICE).

Supply, quality and regulation

The availability of animal-assisted activities and therapies depends on the individual's needs, type of activity or therapy and the waiting list. For example, dolphin therapy is only available at specialist facilities in specific overseas locations. On the other hand, a number of organisations provide assistance dogs, but some of these organisations have a substantial waiting list.

Some nationally recognised credentials and regulations are available for the providers of some animal-assisted activities and therapies in the UK. For example, the Association of Chartered Physiotherapists in Therapeutic Riding runs a one year course for chartered physiotherapists who wish to deliver hippotherapy and therapeutic horse-riding (4). No nationally recognised credentials or regulations exist for the providers of some of the other animal-based therapies such as dolphin therapy.

Costs and time

Costs: the costs vary depending on the type of intervention and the needs of the individual participant. For example, dolphin therapy can cost anything from £1,000–10,000 depending on the specific programme, the type of activity undertaken, the number of sessions, and the costs of foreign travel and accommodation (5).

Time: the amount of time required will depend on the specific type of intervention. Some interventions, such as some forms of equine-assisted therapy, may be delivered over several weeks, with each session lasting an hour or so. On the other hand, assistance dogs live with the person with autism full-time for many years (6, 7).

Risks

Some risks are associated with animal-based activities and therapies. The risks of injury to humans are largely as a result of unpredicted animal behaviour, although these risks can be minimised through properly researched and correctly implemented programmes. The risks to animals are largely the result of poor animal welfare so vigilance is required to ensure that appropriate standards are maintained.

Specific forms of animal-assisted activities and therapies

Assistance dogs

Introduction

Assistance dogs (also known as service dogs) are specifically trained to help individuals with various types of disability. Their use has now been extended to children with autism.

Some assistance dogs (sometimes called autism assistance dogs) are specially trained to assist in the day-to-day life of the family with a child with autism. It is important that the dog is recognised as a 'working dog' and to this end the dog will work in a special harness that connects them to both the parent and the child.

The dogs are trained to lead, acting on instructions from the parent, while the child is encouraged to walk alongside the dog using a harness attached to the dog (7, 8).

> ### Assistance dogs
>
> **Definition:** dogs specially trained to act as a companion to the child with autism.
>
> **Aims:** to encourage independence and safety, to encourage communication, social skills, to enhance inclusion.
>
> **Who:** children on the spectrum who can cope with an active, lively animal, day in, day out for many years.
>
> **Evidence:** insufficient evidence to determine if assistance dogs have any benefits.
>
> **Risks:** some risks of the dog biting or scratching the child with autism, or the child with autism hurting or injuring the dog.

Aims

Assistance dogs are normally used by children on the autism spectrum who can cope with an active animal day in, day out for many years.

The use of autism assistance dogs is based on the idea that the dogs offer greater independence to the child and parent, while ensuring the child is safe if they become stressed or anxious.

The supporters of assistance dogs have made a variety of claims for their use with children on the autism spectrum. For example, some people have claimed that the dogs offer greater independence to the child and parent, while ensuring the child is safe if they become stressed or anxious. Some people have claimed that the dogs may also offer other benefits, such as encouraging the child to communicate and be more sociable and in enhancing the opportunities for the inclusion of the child and family in society (7, 8).

Evidence

Determining the benefits of assistance dogs for children on the autism spectrum is not currently possible. We must wait for further research of sufficiently high quality to be completed (9).

Risks

Some possible hazards include the dog biting or scratching the child with autism or the person with autism hurting or injuring the dog. Because of this, assistance dogs are carefully selected for their placidity and resilience. Supervision is also essential in creating a placement that is safe and effective. The carers of any child must understand that their role is to ensure that the relationship between the child and dog is consistently gentle and mutually enjoyable.

Assistance dogs may not be appropriate for children who are allergic to dogs, frightened of dogs, may hurt or frighten dogs (however inadvertently) and families who cannot cope with the costs, effort and logistics required to train and look after a dog on a long-term basis (7, 8).

Dolphin therapy

Introduction

The simplest kind of dolphin therapy involves the child swimming with, touching or 'looking after' dolphins. The more complex therapies, such as dolphin-assisted therapy (DAT), are based on structured programmes which are supposedly designed to meet the needs of the individual child. In DAT the child is encouraged to complete one or more pre-determined tasks, such as placing a ring on a peg or saying a word. If the child completes the task to a satisfactory standard, they are rewarded by being allowed to interact with a dolphin. This interaction may include touching or kissing the dolphin, or getting in the water and taking a ride holding onto the dolphin's dorsal fin (10).

Dolphin therapy

Definition: an intervention which involves interacting with dolphins.

Aims: ranges from 'correcting the human psycho-emotional state' to helping a child to increase their attention and to engage in responses in their child's individualised programme.

Who: people with autism of any age and any level of ability.

Evidence: insufficient evidence to determine if dolphin therapy has any benefits.

Risks: some risks of injury as a result of aggressive behaviour from the dolphin, and risks of diseases transmitted from the dolphin.

Aims

Dolphin therapy is undertaken by people on the autism spectrum of any age and any level of ability.

Some people claim that dolphin therapy is designed to correct the 'human psycho-emotional state'. Others claim that the desire to interact with the dolphin will increase a child's attention to relevant stimuli and encourage the child to engage in responses within the child's individualised programme.

Some people claim that dolphin therapy works because the dolphin's high frequency means of communication, known as ultrasound, affects human tissue and cell structure, which can alter brain-wave patterns in humans, or that dolphin therapy generates intense emotions of 'love and connection to nature' (10, 11, 12).

Evidence

Determining the benefits of dolphin therapy for individuals on the autism spectrum is not currently possible. We must wait for further research of sufficiently high quality to be completed.

No evidence supports the claims that dolphin therapy can alter brain-wave patterns in humans (13).

Risks

Risks include aggressive behaviour by dolphins, transmission of diseases from dolphins, and drowning. If the therapy takes place in the open sea, additional hazards include adverse sea conditions, boat traffic and harmful sea creatures.

There are also risks to the dolphins such as stress in captive dolphins, transmission of diseases from humans and pressure on wild dolphin populations (5).

Equine-assisted activities and therapies

Introduction

Equine-assisted activities and therapies (EAAT) describe any intervention using horses or the horses' environment.

Equine-assisted activities include a wide range of horse-related activities (such as therapeutic horse-riding, interactive vaulting, therapeutic carriage driving, as well as grooming and stable management).

Equine-assisted therapies include hippotherapy (use of a horse to improve neurological function and sensory processing) and equine-assisted psychotherapy (use of a horse to improve mental health).

EAAT differs from horse-riding for pleasure in that the therapist uses horses and the horses' environment for specific therapeutic purposes (14)

Aims

Therapeutic horse-riding is primarily designed to improve physical, psychological, cognitive, and social skills, as well as to improve horsemanship skills. It is used with a wide variety of people with a range of different conditions.

Hippotherapy is primarily designed to improve neurological function and sensory processing. It is often used with people who have neurological or sensory processing difficulties, such as people with cerebral palsy or brain injury.

Equine-facilitated psychotherapy is primarily designed to help personal exploration (such as awareness of thoughts, emotions, and behaviours) through interactions with the horse. It is often used with people with emotional, behavioural or mental health problems (15, 16, 17).

Equine-assisted therapy

Definition: any kind of treatment that incorporates activities using horses or the horses' environment.

Aims: to provide one or more therapeutic benefits, such as to improve posture, social interaction and planning skills.

Who: people with autism of all ages and level of ability.

Evidence: extremely limited amount of research evidence that equine-assisted therapy may provide some benefits.

Risks: some risks such as injury associated with falling off the horse.

Evidence

Therapeutic horse-riding may provide some benefits for some individuals on the autism spectrum according to an extremely limited amount of research evidence of sufficiently high quality (3). Determining the benefits of other forms of equine-assisted activities and therapies for individuals on the autism spectrum is not currently possible. We must wait for further research of sufficiently high quality to be completed.

Risks

Some risks are associated with EAAT, such as injury associated with falling off the horse, being bitten, kicked, trodden on etc. Psychological stress might arise if the individual becomes intimidated by the horse or its behaviour.

Further information

In this book: Please see How to use this book (page 11), Chapter 3 (page 38) for information about interventions, Chapter 4 (page 43) for information about how scientists evaluate those interventions, and Section 3 (page 284) for advice on making the decision about whether or not to use a specific intervention.

Website: Please see www.researchautism.net/animal-assisted activities and therapies for information about different social care services including information about specific services and details of scientific studies and trials.

References

1. Foden T (2011) *Dogs, Horses and ASD: What are animal-assisted therapies?* Baltimore, MD: IAN Network.

2. O'Haire ME (2013) Animal-assisted intervention for autism spectrum disorder: a systematic literature review. *Journal of Autism and Developmental Disorders* **43** 1606–1622.

3. Research Autism (2014) *Equine assisted activities and therapies and autism* [online]. Available at: www.researchautism.net/eaat-and-autism (accessed January 13, 2015).

4. Association of Chartered Physiotherapists in therapeutic riding. *ACPTR Hippotherapy Course* (HT) [online]. Available at: http://acptr.csp.org.uk/acptr-hippotherapy-course (accessed 23 March, 2015).

5. Brakes P & Williamson C (2007) *Can you put your faith in DAT?* Chippenham, Wiltshire: Whale and Dolphin Conservation Society.

6. Gabriels RL, Agnew JA, Holt KD, Shoffner A, Zhaoxing P, Ruzzano S, Clayton GH & Mesibov G (2012) Pilot study measuring the effects of therapeutic horseback riding on school-age children and adolescents with autism spectrum disorders. *Research in Autism Spectrum Disorders* **6** 578–588.

7. 4 Paws for Ability (2001) *Autism Service Dogs*. Xenia, OH: 4 Paws for Ability.

8. Berry A, Borgi M, Francia N & Alleva EFC (2013) Use of assistance and therapy dogs for children with autism spectrum disorders: a critical review of the current evidence. *Journal of Alternative and Complementary Medicine* **19** 73–80.

9. Research Autism (2014) *Assistance dogs and autism* [online]. Available at: www.researchautism.net/assistance-dogs-and-autism (accessed January 13, 2015).

10. Fiksdal BL, Houlihan D & Barnes AC (2012) Dolphin-assisted therapy: claims versus evidence. *Autism Research and Treatment* 839792.

11. Lukina LN (1999) Influence of dolphin-assisted therapy sessions on the functional state of children with psychoneurological symptoms of disease. *Human Psychology* **25** 676–679.

12. Nathanson DE (1998) Long-term effectiveness of dolphin-assisted therapy for children with severe disabilities. *Anthrozoos: A Multidisciplinary Journal of the Interactions of People & Animals* **11** 22–32.

13. Research Autism (2014) *Dolphin therapy and autism* [online]. Available at: www.researchautism.net/dolphin-therapy-and-autism (accessed January 13, 2015).

14. Professional Association of Therapeutic Horsemanship International (2014) *EAAT definitions*. Denver, CO: Professional Association of Therapeutic Horsemanship International.

15. Professional Association of Therapeutic Horsemanship International (2014) *Learn about therapeutic riding*. Denver, CO: Professional Association of Therapeutic Horsemanship International.

16. Professional Association of Therapeutic Horsemanship International (2014) *Learn about hippotherapy*. Denver, CO: Professional Association of Therapeutic Horsemanship International Read Full (New Window)

17. Professional Association of Therapeutic Horsemanship International (2014) *What is equine facilitated psychotherapy and equine facilitated learning?*. Denver, CO: Professional Association of Therapeutic Horsemanship International.

Chapter 26:
Scientifically unfeasible and potentially harmful interventions

Introduction

There are some interventions which are scientifically unfeasible and potentially harmful. Some of these are listed in this section. Some of them – such as chelation – are described elsewhere in this book.

Many of these interventions demonstrate the red flags we list on page 302.

We can't emphasise strongly enough that no good reason to try these interventions exists. But we don't expect you to take our word for it: here's the background and the evidence.

Specific interventions

Holding therapy

Holding therapy is a type of attachment therapy used to help children who find it difficult to form a relationship with their mother. The therapy consists of forced holding by a therapist or parent either until the child stops resisting or until a fixed period has elapsed. The carer does not usually release their hold until the child 'surrenders' and looks into the carer's eyes. The carer then returns the child's gaze and exchanges affection.

We believe that the underlying theory for holding therapy, that the bond between mother and child is broken, is fundamentally flawed. We also believe that any intervention that involves force is potentially physically and psychologically harmful.

According to Mercer, 'Attachment therapy (AT) is a mental health intervention for children that involves physical restraint and discomfort. Practitioners base its use on the assumption that rage resulting from early frustration and mistreatment must be provoked and released in order for the child to form an emotional attachment and become affectionate and obedient' (1).

Despite claims from AT practitioners, there is no research evidence to support the use of AT. Furthermore, there is a risk of death and injury from AT (1, 2).

Miracle mineral solution

Miracle mineral solution (MMS) (also known as chlorine dioxide solution) is a 28% sodium chlorite solution diluted in lemon juice. This results in the formation of chlorine dioxide, a potent bleach, which is then either given as a drink or an enema. Some people think that it can be used to treat a number of unrelated conditions such as HIV, hepatitis, cancer, and autism.

No scientific evidence exists that shows miracle mineral solution is an effective intervention for any condition. Furthermore, ingesting bleach is harmful. The Food and Drug Administration in the US provides the following guidance:

'High oral doses of this bleach, such as those recommended in the labelling, can cause nausea, vomiting, diarrhoea, and symptoms of severe dehydration. [...] Consumers who have MMS should stop using it immediately and throw it away. The FDA advises consumers who have experienced any negative side effects from MMS to consult a healthcare professional as soon as possible.' (3)

Packing therapy

Packing therapy is an intervention where an individual is wrapped in towels previously soaked in cold water. While the child is wrapped, the therapist can take the opportunity to talk to the child about their feelings. The aim of this intervention is to help children to understand their bodily limits (4).

Packing therapy is scientifically implausible and potentially abusive.

'Against Le Packing: A consensus statement' signed by academics from around the world appeared in the *Journal of the American Academy of Child and Adolescent Psychiatry* in February 2011 and concluded:

'We have reached the consensus that practitioners and families around the world should consider this approach unethical. Furthermore, this "therapy" ignores current knowledge about autism spectrum disorders; goes against evidence-based practice parameters and treatment guidelines published in the United States, Canada, United Kingdom, Spain, Italy, Hungary, and Australia; and, in our view, poses a risk of preventing these children and adolescents from accessing their basic human rights to health and education.' (5)

Testosterone regulation

Testosterone regulation is the use of drugs to reduce the amount of testosterone in the body. It is sometimes used to treat prostate cancer or to help reduce sexually inappropriate behaviour. In autism, it is used because some people believe that autism is caused by heavy metals such as mercury. They believe that androgens, such as testosterone, increase the toxicity of mercury, so reducing the level of testosterone would reduce the effects of this toxicity.

No evidence shows that autism is caused by heavy metals such as mercury. Also, no evidence shows that testosterone regulation helps people with autism. Testosterone regulation could lead to irreversible damage to sexual functioning if administered to children or adolescents (6).

The National Institute for Health and Care Excellence reported:

'Do not use testosterone regulation for the management of core symptoms of autism in adults.' (6)

Further information

In this book: Please see How to use this book (page 11), Chapter 3 (page 38) for information about interventions, Chapter 4 (page 43) for information about how scientists evaluate those interventions, and Section 3 (page 284) for advice on making the decision about whether or not to use a specific intervention.

Website: Please see www.researchautism.net/scientifcally-unfeasible-harmful-interventions for information about different scientifically unfeasible and potentially harmful interventions including information about specific interventions and details of scientific studies and trials.

References

1. Mercer J (2002) Attachment therapy: a treatment without empirical support. *Scientific Review of Mental Health Practice* **1**.

2. Boris NW (2003) Attachment, aggression and holding: a cautionary tale. *Attachment and Human Development* **5** 245–247.

3. US Food and Drug Association (2010) *Miracle Mineral Solution (MMS): Product as consumed produces a potent bleach*. Silver Spring, MD: US Food and Drug Association.

4. Spinney L (2007) Therapy for autistic children causes outcry in France. *Lancet* **370** 645–646.

5. Amaral D, Rogers SJ, Baron-Cohen S, Bourgeron T, Caffo E, Fombonne E, Fuentes J, Howlin P, Rutter M, Klin A, Volkmar F, Lord C, Minshew N, Nardocci F, Rizzolatti G, Russo S, Scifo R & van der Gaag RJ (2011) Against le packing: a consensus statement. *Journal of the American Academy of Child and Adolescent Psychiatry* **50** 191–2.

6. National Institute for Health and Care Excellence (2012) *Autism: Recognition, referral, diagnosis and management of adults on the autism spectrum*. London: National Institute for Health and Care Excellence.

Chapter 27:

Conclusion

Our aim in this book is to give you an honest overview of the range of autism interventions, to look at the research behind those interventions, and to suggest some tools and resources you may like to use when deciding which interventions, if any, you want to use.

Autism

Autism is a condition characterised by two 'core' features:

- persistent difficulties with social communication and social interaction
- restricted, repetitive patterns of behaviour, interests, or activities.

Autism is often referred to as a spectrum because people with autism can be very different from each other. For example, some people may be highly articulate while others may be completely non-verbal. A person with autism can also have an uneven profile of abilities. They may be extremely good at maths, for example, but find it very difficult to travel independently.

Most people on the autism spectrum do not want to be 'cured' but they may want help to deal with practical problems such as talking to other people, crossing the road safely, or finding a job.

Issues

As well as the core features of autism described above, people on the autism spectrum may experience a number of other issues, problems and challenges.

Those problems may include difficulties with cognition (thinking), motor issues such as clumsy gait, or sensory issues such as a profound dislike of certain sounds. They may include difficulties caused by co-occurring conditions such as ADHD or epilepsy. They may include mental health problems such as anxiety or depression.

Choosing Autism Interventions: A Research-Based Guide © Research Autism and Autism West Midlands

Some people on the autism spectrum may also exhibit challenging behaviours. Taken together, these issues can have a considerable impact on the person and on their family.

Interventions

An intervention is any action (such as a treatment or therapy or the provision of a service) which is designed to help people on the autism spectrum (or their parents and carers). Some interventions do not target the core features of autism but instead target one or more of the associated issues.

A large number of interventions are available, many of which aren't supported by scientific research. Some interventions are very expensive, ineffective or potentially harmful.

No interventions can 'cure' autism. No single intervention will help everyone on the autism spectrum. However, some interventions can help some people on the spectrum with some issues.

The most effective interventions share some common principles, such as being based on a good understanding of autism and being tailored to the needs of the individual on the spectrum.

Research

A limited amount of high quality scientific research on interventions for autism exists, but it is slowly growing.

People affected by autism need much more research into autism interventions. Future research should include people on the autism spectrum at every stage of the research process, be scientifically rigorous, include qualitative as well as quantitative studies, include robust outcomes measures, look at specific groups of people on the spectrum, and be published in peer-reviewed journals.

A lack of research evidence supporting some interventions does not mean that they do not work; it may simply mean that more research is needed to find out if they do work.

Evaluating research studies

Evaluating the research evidence is an important part of deciding which intervention to use. Good research can give objective and unbiased information on whether an intervention works, how it works and why, and which groups of people it can help and under which circumstances.

The research process has many advantages but it also has some limitations such as reporting only positive results in the early studies, meaning that it can take many years before a true picture of the effectiveness of an intervention comes out. Also, sometimes using the research is difficult in the real world.

Remember that even if the research suggests that an intervention is effective, it may not work for every person on the autism spectrum.

Making the decision

Deciding which intervention to use should be based not only on the research evidence for an intervention but also on your knowledge of the person with autism and your own circumstances. What works for one family may not work for another.

Because of this, we have provided you with some guidance on other factors to consider when making the decision on which intervention to use.

In section 3 of this book, you can find a range of tools including some principles, some questions to ask, and a summary of the NICE guidance. In section 4, the Appendices, we have also listed some useful resources such as websites, reading materials and organisations which may help.

Keeping up to date

While in this book we comment on the research available at the time of publication, that research does not stand still. Autism research is fast paced, with new information coming out all the time.

If you want to keep yourself up to date you can do so by checking the latest research on the Research Autism website at www.researchautism.net/latest-publications

We welcome your feedback on this book. Please contact us about any new interventions or any new research on a current intervention by emailing info@researchautism.net. Thank you.

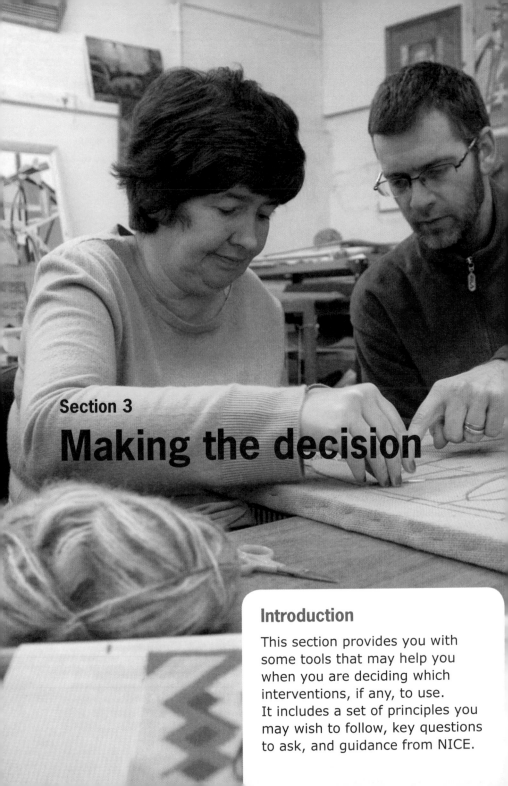

Section 3

Making the decision

Introduction

This section provides you with some tools that may help you when you are deciding which interventions, if any, to use. It includes a set of principles you may wish to follow, key questions to ask, and guidance from NICE.

Introduction

Lots of interventions are out there, and you need to workout which ones are right for you (that's probably why you're reading this!).

We're going to look at taking charge of the decision and then look at some tools that may help you to make that decision.

Taking charge

Ultimately, you will be making the decision about which interventions to use. A number of things you can do to take charge of the decision-making are:

- Do some research – find out what the scientific evidence says about the therapy, including whether it works or not.

- Become an informed consumer – find out how much the intervention really costs, how much time it takes, and if there are any potential hazards.

- Choose the practitioner or programme carefully – especially if you are thinking of using a practitioner or a programme that is unregulated.

- Tell your practitioner about all of the interventions you are receiving. Giving them a full picture of what you are doing will help them to ensure you receive co-ordinated and safe care.

- Remember that you have rights – whether you are a patient, a parent or a customer. Make sure you get answers to your questions.

The tools

In the following pages we provide a number of tools that may help you to make your decision. These tools include:

- further details on the key principles that we believe any intervention should follow

- a list of key questions that you may like to ask about any intervention

- a list of red flags (signs that an intervention is not what it seems)

- a list of key questions you may like to ask about research papers
- a summary of the most recent guidance from the National Institute for Health and Care Excellence (NICE).

Please remember that these tools can only guide you, they can't tell you what you should or should not do. And bear in mind that each person on the autism spectrum is a unique individual, with different needs and abilities. What works for one person on the autism spectrum may not work for another.

Key principles for autism interventions: additional information

We want to explain a bit more about the key principles for autism interventions and why we think they are important (page 14 of this book).

1. The intervention is based on a good understanding of autism

Some interventions are based on flawed theories of autism and the causes of autism. For example, some of the first interventions to be used were based on the incorrect belief that autism is caused by so-called 'refrigerator mothers': mothers whose denial of emotional warmth causes their babies to turn away from other human beings and become autistic. We now know that this theory is false. Most researchers believe that autism has a variety of causes, which are likely to be a complex mix of genetic and environmental factors that affect a number of different areas of the brain (1, 2).

Other interventions are designed to 'cure' autism, despite the fact that autism is not an illness or a disease. These interventions do not usually consider how different each person is from others on the spectrum, and none has been shown to work (3). Furthermore, the idea of curing autism goes against the views of some in the autism community who do not want to be cured and would rather that research funding be spent on helping with practical problems such as crossing the road safely, making friends, or finding a job (4).

2. The people who deliver the intervention know the person well and respect their feelings and views

People who deliver an intervention should know the person they are working with well – because every person on the autism spectrum is different. People who deliver an intervention should also respect the person's feelings and views. For example, the National Institute for Health and Care Excellence recommended that:

'All health and social care professionals providing care and support for adults with autism should:

- aim to foster the person's autonomy, promote active participation in decisions about care and support self-management
- maintain continuity of individual relationships wherever possible
- ensure that comprehensive information about the nature of, and interventions and services for, their difficulties is available in an appropriate language or format including various visual, verbal and aural, easy-read, and different colour and font formats)
- consider whether the person may benefit from access to a trained advocate.

One study found that some support staff in some care settings can make assumptions about the people they care for. This could stop them from understanding their views and wishes (6).

When this happens, people with autism could potentially be subjected to abuse. The Winterbourne View scandal is an example of what can happen when this is allowed to continue (7).

3. The person's capacity for consent is taken into account.

Some people on the autism spectrum lack the capacity to consent to interventions. However, they still have the right to be protected from interventions which are painful, hazardous or unduly distressing. That right is enshrined in various pieces of legislation such as the Age of Legal Capacity (Scotland) Act

(1991), the Children Act (1989), the Mental Capacity Act (2005) and the Mental Health Act (1983) (8, 9).

For example, the Mental Capacity Act (2005) applies to everyone who looks after, or cares for, individuals aged 16 and over who lack capacity to make particular decisions for themselves. This includes family carers, healthcare staff, social care staff, and a range of other people.

The Act states that adults who lack capacity have the right to be represented by an advocate during any discussions of interventions. The advocate must ensure their rights are upheld. Safeguarding procedures must be kept in mind if the intervention has known risks (10).

4. The intervention is adapted to the needs of the person receiving it

Interventions should be adapted to meet the needs of the individual on the autism spectrum because each person on the spectrum is so different.

For example, some people on the autism spectrum have over-sensitive senses. They may find certain sounds physically painful or they may not be able to wear certain clothing because they find the fabric uncomfortable. Some people on the autism spectrum have under-sensitivity. They may seek out strong flavours, as they are unable to taste bland food, or they may rock or spin to stimulate their senses of movement and balance.

So, an intervention designed to help someone on the autism spectrum deal with their sensory sensitivities would need to take into account the specific sensitivities of each individual (11).

Also, some interventions not originally designed for people on the autism spectrum can still be beneficial to them if they have been adapted to their needs.

For example, the National Institute for Health and Care Excellence recommended that cognitive behavioural therapy should be adapted for individuals with autism. This might include, for example, using 'a more concrete and structured approach with a greater use of written and visual information (which may include worksheets, thought bubbles, images and "tool boxes")' and 'placing greater emphasis on changing behaviour, rather than [thoughts], and using the behaviour as the starting point for intervention' (5).

5. The intervention is based on a theory that is logical and scientifically feasible

A number of interventions for people on the autism spectrum are based on illogical and unfeasible theories. Sometimes these are flawed theories about the nature of autism (see principle 1) and sometimes these are flawed theories about how the intervention itself is supposed to work.

One intervention that is scientifically unfeasible is homeopathy. According to the NHS Choices website: 'There have been several reviews of the scientific evidence on the effectiveness of homeopathy. The House of Commons Science and Technology Committee said there is no evidence that homeopathy is effective as a treatment for any health condition.

'The ideas that underpin homeopathy are not accepted by mainstream science, and are not consistent with long-accepted principles on the way that the physical world works. The Committee's 2010 report on homeopathy said the "like cures like" principle [homeopathy's central principle] is "theoretically weak", and that this is the "settled view of medical science"' (12).

6. Research evidence shows the intervention can work for people on the autism spectrum

Evidence-based interventions are important as the evidence provides assurances that they have been tested, and that they have been assessed for risks. Remember: evidence in favour of an intervention does not guarantee that it works with every person with autism, but it does provide some reassurance to people who are thinking about using it.

Many interventions used with people on the autism spectrum (including many forms of adaptive and assistive technology such as computer apps, smart phones and visual schedules) have limited or no research evidence. This does not mean that they do not work; it may simply mean that more research is required to find out if they do work.

Also, remember that some interventions (often not evidence-based) are marketed to play on a person's guilt or anxieties to convince them to pay to use this provider of the intervention. These interventions may not be designed with the person specifically in mind, may not work and often risk people's time and money (13).

7. The intervention works in the real world, not just in a research laboratory

Interventions should work in the real world. Many autism interventions start off being tested in research settings – where as many variables as possible are controlled. However, in the real world, it is often not possible to control for things like the level of training and experience of the person giving the intervention, the room where the intervention takes place, how often it can take place, and who takes part in the intervention. Because of this, a number of interventions have been shown to be less effective in the real world compared to research settings. For example, some forms of theory of mind training have been shown to be effective in laboratory settings, but seem to be ineffective in real-life situations (13).

8. The intervention is delivered by, or supported by, appropriately qualified and experienced professionals

Where the intervention is delivered by professionals, it is important that they have the appropriate qualifications to deliver the intervention effectively. For example, in the UK, allied healthcare professionals (such as speech and language therapists) are regulated by the Health and Care Professions Council and may also be chartered with an appropriate professional association (such as the Royal College of Speech and Language Therapists). These agencies try to ensure that allied health professionals follow best practice, such as using evidence-based interventions.

Please note: unfortunately there is no regulation for some 'professionals' such as homeopaths, and no evidence that some practices such as homeopathy work, so any advice from these 'professionals' should be treated with extreme caution (12).

It is important that, in addition to any professional training, professionals have an appropriate level of experience, that is, they have actually worked successfully with people on the autism spectrum. It is equally important that they have the right attitude, that is, they 'get' autism and they 'get' people on the autism spectrum.

Where the intervention is delivered by someone on the autism spectrum or by family members, it is important that they are supported by appropriately qualified professionals. For example, anyone thinking of following a special diet should seek advice from a paediatrician, GP or dietitian. This is because altering your diet can have significant, long-term effects. According to one review of special diets for people on the autism spectrum:

'The combination of food selectivity and restrictive diets can make it difficult to achieve an adequate diet, consequently resulting in an excessive intake of certain foods and/or deficiencies and malnutrition due to insufficient amounts of other foods. In turn, inadequate intakes may lead to the development of chronic and degenerative conditions that tend to appear in the third or fourth decade of life (cardiovascular disease, high blood pressure, diabetes, dyslipidemia [imbalance of fats], and osteoporosis [fragile bones], among others) or even earlier, in the case of menstrual disturbances, sleep apnea [pauses in breathing], and psychosocial disorders.' (15)

9. The people delivering the intervention follow established guidance

The people delivering the intervention should follow established guidance, especially when that guidance has been published by relevant regulating bodies or is based on research evidence.

For example, in the UK, psychiatrists and paediatricians who prescribe antipsychotics for people on the autism spectrum are expected to follow guidance on their use published by the Medicines and Healthcare Products Regulatory Agency (16). Recommendations on specific dosages for specific antipsychotics are set out in publications such as the BNF (British National Formulary) (17).

Where interventions are not covered by regulating bodies, the people delivering those interventions should still follow established guidance, especially when that guidance is based on research evidence. For example, in the UK, the National Institute for Health and Care Excellence has published guidance on interventions for adults on the autism spectrum and for children and young people on the autism spectrum (15, 18). (Please see page 308).

It is also helpful if the people delivering a specific intervention follow any guidance (usually set out in the form of a manual of instructions) from the developers of the intervention. This guidance will normally explain the key principles behind the intervention and how it should be delivered. Following the guidance ensures that the intervention is actually delivered the way it is supposed to be.

10. The intervention is carefully monitored and reviewed on a regular basis

All interventions should be carefully monitored and reviewed on a regular basis to ensure that they are delivering real benefits, using robust outcome measures. If it becomes clear that there are no significant benefits, the intervention should be stopped or amended.

For example, the National Institute for Health and Care Excellence recommended that, if antipsychotic medication is prescribed to help children on the autism spectrum with challenging behaviours, the paediatrician or psychiatrist should:

- 'identify the target behaviour

- decide on an appropriate measure to monitor effectiveness, including frequency and severity of the behaviour and a measure of global impact
- review the effectiveness and any side effects of the medication after three-to-four weeks
- stop treatment if there is no indication of a clinically important response at six weeks.' (18)

11. The intervention provides significant benefits

Interventions should provide significant benefits to the individual on the autism spectrum (and their family or carers). However, different people may have different views on what counts as a significant benefit.

For example, a recent study of weighted blankets reported that a weighted blanket 'did not help children with ASD sleep for a longer period of time, fall asleep significantly faster, or wake less often. However, the weighted blanket was favoured by children and parents, and blankets were well tolerated over this period'. (19)

In other words, the researchers did not think that the weighted blankets provided any significant benefits but the parents did and wanted to keep them. This may be because the parents saw some changes in the child that the study was not measuring, such as making the child calmer. Or it could be that the parents thought they saw some benefits that were not actually there (19).

Some interventions have not yet shown long-lasting benefits. For example, some treatments (such as oxytocin, a hormone that is injected or inhaled) have shown improvements in behaviours and communication skills, but only for a brief period after the treatment was given. When the treatment is stopped, the measured improvements in behaviour are lost (20).

12. The intervention does not cause significant physical or emotional harm

Some interventions have a major risk of physical or emotional harm. For example, holding therapy is a type of attachment therapy. It is forced holding by a therapist or parent, either until the child stops resisting or until a fixed period has elapsed. The carer does not usually release their hold until the child 'surrenders' and looks into the carer's eyes. The carer then returns the child's gaze and exchanges affection.

According to Mercer, 'Practitioners base its use on the assumption that rage resulting from early frustration and mistreatment must be provoked and released in order for the child to form an emotional attachment and become affectionate and obedient. Death and injury have resulted from attachment therapy.' (21)

Holding therapy is a good example of an intervention which can cause physical harm through the forced holding, as well as emotional harm through the act of forcing a child to 'surrender' and look into their parent's eyes.

13. The benefits outweigh any costs (including risks)

Weighing up any potential costs (including any risks) against any potential benefits for an intervention is likely to be up to each person to decide, as some may be willing to take on more risk than others.

Some interventions (including some medications) may present significant costs and side effects. For example, a significant amount of research evidence shows that the drug risperidone may be beneficial for the treatment of various problems faced by people on the autism spectrum, including irritability, repetition and hyperactivity.

However, the same research noted that risperidone has many potential side effects, especially weight gain and drowsiness which may have a significant impact on the person's quality of life (22).

14. The intervention is good value for money and time invested

Different people will have different ideas about what is and what is not good value for money. However, some interventions are extremely expensive and we would recommend that you try to identify as many of the costs as you can before undertaking the intervention.

For example, a review of dolphin-assisted therapy (DAT) found that:

'The cost for two weeks of DAT varies a great deal and a variety of packages are available. Figures given by Humphries (2003) quote a typical price of around $2,600 (approximately £1,370) for five 40-minute sessions, but it can cost a participant and one parent more than £3,300 for two weeks, including flights and accommodation. At the more expensive end of the market is the 'Dolphin Human Therapy', which during 2006 cost $7,850 for two weeks, or $11,800 for three weeks. These quoted prices are for the therapy only (fixed sessions per week) and do not include flights and accommodation.

'There are other hidden costs such as surcharges for health care, which should be taken into consideration. Families are generally encouraged to bring children for a minimum of two weeks of DAT. When flights, accommodation and loss of earnings are taken into account, such excursions can cost up to £10,000.' (23)

Further information

In this book: Please see How to use this book (page 11), Chapter 3 (page 38) for information about interventions, Chapter 4 (page 43) for information about how scientists evaluate those interventions, and Section 3 (page 284) for advice on making the decision about whether or not to use a specific intervention.

Website: Please see www.researchautism.net/key-principles for the latest version of these principles.

References

1. Medical Research Council (2001) *MRC Review of Autism Research – Epidemiology and Causes.* London, UK: Medical Research Council.

2. Mercer J (2010) Whose fault is autism? A historical view of placing blame. *Psychology Today.*

3. Bölte S (2014) Is autism curable? *Developmental medicine and child neurology* **56** 927–931.

4. Pellicano L, Dinsmore A & Charman T (2013) *A Future Made Together*. London: Institute of Education.

5. National Institute for Health and Care Excellence (2012) *Autism: Recognition, referral, diagnosis and management of adults on the autism spectrum*. London: National Institute for Health and Care Excellence.

6. Griffith GM, Hutchinson L & Hastings RP (2013) I'm not a patient, I'm a person: the experiences of individuals with intellectual disabilities and challenging behavior –a thematic synthesis of qualitative studies. *Clinical Psychology: Science and practice* **20** 469–488.

7. Cafe R (2012) Winterbourne View: Abuse footage shocked nation. *BBC News*. Available at: www.bbc.co.uk/news/uk-england-bristol-20084254 (accessed January 13, 2015).

8. Tidy J (2012) *Consent To Treatment (Mental Capacity and Mental Health Legislation)* [online]. Available at: www.patient.co.uk/doctor/consent-to-treatment-mental-capacity-and-mental-health-legislation (accessed January 13, 2015).

9. Knott L (2011) *Consent to Treatment in Children (Mental Capacity and Mental Health Legislation)* [online]. Available at: www.patient.co.uk/doctor/consent-to-treatment-in-children-mental-capacity-and-mental-health-legislation (accessed January 13, 2015).

10. Mental Capacity Act Code of Practice (2007). London: Department for Constitutional Affairs.

11. Marco EJ, Hinkley LBN, Hill SS & Nagarajan SS (2011) Sensory processing in autism: a review of neurophysiologic findings. *Pediatric Research* **69** 48R–54R.

12. NHS Choices (2013) *Homeopathy*. London: NHS.

13. Research Autism (2013) *Introduction to interventions for autism* [online]. Available at: http://researchautism.net/introduction-autism-interventions (accessed January 13, 2015).

14. Fletcher-Watson S *et al* (2014) *Interventions based on the theory of mind cognitive model for autism spectrum disorder (ASD)*. Cochrane Database of Systematic Reviews

15. Marí-Bauset S, Zazpe I, Marí-Sanchis A, Llopis-González A & Suárez-Varela MM (2015) Anthropometric measurements and nutritional assessment in autism spectrum disorders: a systematic review. *Research in Autism Spectrum Disorders* **9** 130–143.

16. Medicines and Healthcare Products Agency (2013) *Antipsychotic Drugs* London: Medicines and Healthcare Products Regulatory Agency.

17. British National Formulary (2014). London: BNF.

18. National Institute for Health and Care Excellence (2013) *The Management and Support of Children and Young People on the Autism Spectrum* London: National Institute for Health and Care Excellence.

19. Gringras P, Green D, Wright B, Rush C, Sparrowhawk M, Pratt K, Allgar V, Hooke N, Moore D, Zaiwalla Z & Wiggs L (2014) Weighted Blankets and Sleep in Autistic Children – A Randomized Controlled Trial. *Pediatrics* **134** (2) 298–306.

20. Preti A, Melis M, Siddi S, Vellante M, Doneddu G & Fadda R (2014) Oxytocin and autism: a systematic review of randomized controlled trials. *Journal of Child and Adolescent Psychopharmacology* **24** 54–68.

21. Mercer J (2002) Attachment therapy: a treatment without empirical support. *Scientific Review of Mental Health Practice* **1** (2).

22. Jesner O, Aref-Adib M & Coren E (2007) Risperidone for autism spectrum disorder. *Cochrane Database of Systematic Reviews* **24** CD005040.

23. Brakes P & Williamson C (2007) *Can you Put Your Faith in DAT?* Chippenham, Wiltshire: Whale and Dolphin Conservation Society.

Key questions to consider when choosing an intervention

Background
What is the full name of the intervention or programme? Does it have any other names?
How was the intervention developed? (For example is it based on clinical or personal experience, religious or philosophical belief, does it come from another field of medicine or disability?)
Were people on the autism spectrum actively involved in, or consulted on, its development?

Philosophy and aims
What is the aim of the intervention or programme?
What is the underlying idea or philosophy behind the intervention or programme?
What is the underlying mechanism, that is, how is it supposed to work?
Does it focus on one specific skill or problem or is it a general approach?
Are you happy with the philosophy and aims of the intervention or programme?

Key features
What type of intervention is it? (Is it a training programme, a special diet, a medication or a service?)
What are the major features of the intervention or programme? For example: • Who delivers the intervention? • Where is it delivered? • How is the intervention delivered?
Is the intervention or programme adapted to the needs of people on the autism spectrum? If so, how?
Is the intervention or programme personalised to the needs of the individual? If so, how?
How is it different to any similar interventions or programmes?
Will I have to undertake or stop other treatments or activities if I start this?

Evidence
What evidence is there for this intervention? (Research studies, personal accounts from other people?)
Are you happy with the level of evidence?

Participants
Which group of people is this intervention or programme supposed to help? (Anyone, people on the autism spectrum, children?)
Are there any people who should not undertake this intervention or programme – such as people with epilepsy or other medical conditions?

Supply and availability
Is this intervention available throughout the UK, only in certain places in the UK, or only overseas?
Which organisations and individuals provide this intervention or programme? If there is more than one supplier, what is the difference between the suppliers?
Is there a waiting list? If so, how long is it and do I have to make a payment to be put on it?

Training
Do I need any training in order to undertake this intervention or programme?
Who provides this training, what does it involve, how long does it take, and how much does it cost?

Equipment and materials
Do I need to buy or rent any special equipment or materials?
Do I need to make any special adaptations or modification to my home?

Time
How long does the intervention or programme last – days, weeks, months, years? (Maximum? Minimum?) How often does it take place (hourly, daily, weekly, monthly)?
How much time is involved over the course of a month (or year, including travel, training and any follow up activities) – for the participant, parents, carers, and professionals?

Costs
Do I have to pay for this intervention or programme? Can I get help to pay for this intervention from anywhere? If so, where?

How much in total does the intervention cost (including enrolment fee, training, materials or equipment (including renewals), fees, administration charges, travel costs, follow up or recurring costs such as re-registration, other additional costs)?
Can I get my money back if the intervention or programme is not effective?

Risks and safety

Does the intervention or programme use techniques that are: • painful or hazardous • distressing for the participants • socially unacceptable (such as sanction-based or restricting liberty) • illegal (such as physical assault, confinement or use of illegal substances)?
Does this intervention or programme have any side effects for the participants or effects for other members of the family (such as increased anxiety or stress)?

Staffing

What is the background of the programme director and staff?
Which staff will be working with me or my child and can I meet them before making my decision?
What experience do these staff have of working with people like me or my child?
Do programme staff co-ordinate their work for me or my child with other professionals?

Regulation and complaints

Is this intervention or programme regulated by an external organisation, such as a professional association or university? If so, when was the date of the last audit and what did it say?
Is there a complaints process? Have there been any complaints or legal disputes about the intervention or programme? What were the outcomes of those complaints or disputes?

Evaluation

What do people say about the intervention (including the providers, people on the spectrum, parents, independent professionals, research evidence)?
Are programme staff open to suggestions about improvements from people on the autism spectrum, families and other professionals?
Can I talk to other people (such as individuals on the autism spectrum, parents) who have been involved with the intervention?

Red flags: signs that an intervention or programme may not be what it seems

⚑	Celebrity endorsement (why should celebrities know more than you?)
⚑	Glitzy presentations (for example videos and PowerPoint presentation) which include bogus scientific data.
⚑	Commercialisation of the intervention or programme (expensive fees or opportunities for you to make money by becoming a re-seller of the intervention).
⚑	'Research' findings that have not been published in reputable peer-reviewed journals.
⚑	Use of outdated or incomplete research studies and reviews which don't show the full picture.
⚑	Hard-sell techniques (including emotional blackmail or special offers).
⚑	Use of words like 'miracle', 'faith', 'trust', 'cure', 'recovery'.
⚑	Claims of high success rates and rapid results.
⚑	Claims that the intervention is effective for many conditions, disorders and diseases.
⚑	Claims that the intervention is easy to use, requiring little training or expertise.
⚑	Claims that other proven interventions are unnecessary, inferior or harmful.
⚑	Warnings and reprimands from appropriate organisations, such as the National Institute for Health and Care Excellence or the Advertising Standards Authority.

Remember: if an intervention looks too good to be true then it probably is.

(These questions and flags are adapted from materials originally developed by Richard Mills, who was indebted to Dr Judith Gould, Professor Gary Mesibov, Professor Patricia Howlin, Damian Milton, Bernard Fleming and the late Dr Lorna Wing and the late Professor Eric Schopler.)

Key questions to ask about any research study

This table lists questions you may like to ask when you are trying to work out how scientifically rigorous a specific research study is.

The more ticks in the 'yes' column, the more likely the study will be valid and reliable – although this is only a very rough rule of thumb.

Please note: Scientists never draw firm conclusions from just one study or set of results. They consider the contribution it makes in the context of other work and their own experience.

Key questions	Yes	No	Maybe/ Partly
Peer review			
Has the study been reviewed by other scientists who are independent of the original research team?			
The peer review process helps to ensure that the information presented in a research study is scientifically rigorous because it has been checked by other scientists.			
The hypothesis (theory)			
Does the study set out a clear hypothesis and clear predictions of what should happen?			
A well-defined and specific research question is more likely to provide useful information than a question that is vague and poorly-defined.			
The researchers			
Are the researchers objective and unbiased?			
Some researchers may be setting out to prove that an intervention works, irrespective of what the data in their research shows. Other researchers may stand to gain financially if, for example, they are providers of the intervention.			
Is the study being run by several different research teams at several different sites at the same time?			
A study run by different research teams on different sites is less likely to be biased than a study run by a single team on the same site.			

Key questions *continued*	Yes	No	Maybe/ Partly
The participants			
Does the study include enough participants to make the results meaningful?			
If the study does not include enough participants the results may not be statistically significant or applicable to other people. (Please see Note 1 at the end of this section.)			
Does the study record important information about the participants, such as the specific diagnosis, any co-occurring conditions, their ages, their intellectual ability, and so on?			
It is important to record important information about the participants as this could affect the results of the intervention. For example, some interventions may not be effective for particular groups of people.			
Does the study include a control group? That is, a group of participants who do not receive the same treatment as the experimental group or who receive a different form of the same treatment?			
A control group is important because it can help to show that any changes in the experimental group are likely to be as a result of the intervention.			
Does the study record important information about the control group, so that you can tell if they were similar or not to the experimental group?			
If the control group is not the same as the experimental group any differences in the results may not be the result of the treatment.			
Were the participants randomised between the experimental group and the control group?			
Randomisation ensures that no one is able to influence who is put in which group and this reduces the risk of bias.			

Key questions *continued*	Yes	No	Maybe/ Partly
The interventions			
Does the study provide enough detail about the intervention and how it was delivered – such as who delivered it, where and when, for how long and how often, and any specific techniques used?			
This makes it easier for other researchers to replicate the study and check whether the findings are accurate.			
Does the study provide enough information about the interventions received by the control group – if there is one?			
In some studies, the control group may be accessing other types of interventions, which may be having their own effects. Not reporting these makes it difficult to compare the effects of the intervention given to the treatment group compared to what the control group is receiving.			
Are the participants (and any parents/carers) blind to the intervention? That is, are they unaware of which intervention they received?			
Blinding ensures that the participants (and any parent/carers) do not behave in a particular way because they know which treatment they are receiving, which could alter the results of the study.			
Are the assessors blind to the intervention, that is, are they unaware of which intervention the participants received?			
Blinding ensures that the assessors do not make judgements about the success of the intervention based on their beliefs about which participants are receiving which treatments.			

Key questions *continued*	Yes	No	Maybe/Partly
The measures			
Does the study use widely recognised and relevant outcome measures?			
Using widely recognised and relevant outcome measures ensures that the results are more likely to be valid and that they can be interpreted by other researchers.			
Does the study use the same measures before and after the intervention?			
If the study uses different measures before and after it can be difficult to compare the effect of the intervention.			
Statistical analysis			
Does the study use statistical techniques that are appropriate to the design of the study?			
Using appropriate and widely-accepted statistical techniques means that any results reported in the study are more likely to be valid and reliable.			

The following questions do not necessarily tell you how scientifically rigorous a specific research study is. But they are important questions you may want to ask anyway.

Other questions	Yes	No	Maybe /Partly
Ethical approval			
Did the study receive ethical approval from an appropriate agency, such as a university?			
Ethical approval safeguards the rights of participants to be treated as openly and fairly as possible within the research, and to consent fully to taking part.			

Other questions *continued*	Yes	No	Maybe /Partly
Inclusion			
Does the research team include anyone on the autism spectrum?			
Including people on the autism spectrum on the research team, rather than just using them as study participants, means that the study is more likely to be of relevance to other people on the autism spectrum.			
Social validity			
Is the research study socially valid, that is, is it likely to produce any benefits in the real world?			
Many research studies ask purely theoretical questions that have no practical application to people on the autism spectrum, their parents/ carers or service providers.			

Note 1: There is no general agreement on how many participants is 'enough' for a research study because it depends on so many other factors. So some researchers may believe that three participants is enough – provided they are part of a study that uses a reasonably robust design, such as a multiple baseline design (1). Other researchers may believe that a minimum of 60 participants is required – provided they are part of a study that uses a very robust design, such as a randomised controlled trial (2).

> **Further information**
>
> **In this book:** Please see Chapter 4 (page 43) for information about how scientists evaluate interventions.

References

1. Cannella-Malone H, Tullis CA & Kazee AR (2011) Using antecedent exercise to decrease challenging behavior in boys with developmental disabilities and an emotional disorder. *Journal of Positive Behavior Interventions* **13** (4) pp. 230–239.

2. Carter AS *et al* (2011) A randomized controlled trial of Hanen's More Than Words in toddlers with early autism symptoms. *Journal of Child Psychology and Psychiatry and Allied Disciplines* **52** (7) pp. 741–752.

Summary of NICE guidance

The National Institute for Health and Care Excellence (NICE) is a UK agency which provides national guidance and advice to improve health and social care.

It has published a number of guidance documents on autism. We have summarised some of the key guidance below.

Children and young people

The following extracts on children and young people with autism are from *Autism: The Management and Support of Children and Young People on the Autism Spectrum* (2013). Leicester and London: The British Psychological Society and The Royal College of Psychiatrists.

The extracts are reproduced with permission from the British Psychological Society and the Royal College of Psychiatrists.

NICE clinical guidance on the core symptoms in children and young people with autism

Psychosocial interventions

5.6.1.1 Consider a specific social-communication intervention for the core features of autism in children and young people that includes play-based strategies with parents, carers and teachers to increase joint attention, engagement and reciprocal communication in the child or young person. Strategies should:

- be adjusted to the child or young person's developmental level
- aim to increase the parents', carers', teachers' or peers' understanding of, and sensitivity and responsiveness to, the child or young person's patterns of communication and interaction
- include techniques of therapist modelling and video-interaction feedback
- include techniques to expand the child or young person's communication, interactive play and social routines.

The intervention should be delivered by a trained professional. For pre-school children consider parent, carer or teacher mediation. For school-aged children consider peer mediation.

Pharmacological and dietary interventions

5.6.1.2 Do not use the following interventions for the management of core features of autism in children and young people:

- antipsychotics
- antidepressants
- anticonvulsants
- exclusion diets (such as gluten- or casein-free diets).

Interventions for autism that should not be used in any context

5.6.1.3 Do not use the following interventions to manage autism in any context in children and young people:

- secretin
- chelation
- hyperbaric oxygen therapy.

NICE clinical guidance on co-existing problems in children and young people with autism

Mental health or medical problems

10.1.7.1 Offer psychosocial and pharmacological interventions for the management of coexisting mental health or medical problems in children and young people with autism in line with NICE guidance for children and young people, including:

- antisocial behaviour and conduct disorders in children and young people (NICE clinical guideline 158)
- attention deficit hyperactivity disorder (ADHD) (NICE clinical guideline 72)
- constipation in children and young people (NICE clinical guideline 99)

- depression in children and young people (NICE clinical guideline 28)
- epilepsy (NICE clinical guideline 137)
- obsessive-compulsive disorder (OCD) and body dysmorphic disorder (BDD) (NICE clinical guideline 31)
- post-traumatic stress disorder (PTSD) (NICE clinical guideline 26).

10.1.7.2 Consider the following for children and young people with autism and anxiety who have the verbal and cognitive ability to engage in a cognitive behavioural therapy (CBT) intervention:

- group CBT adjusted to the needs of children and young people with autism
- individual CBT for children and young people who find group-based activities difficult.

10.1.7.3 Consider adapting the method of delivery of CBT for children and young people with autism and anxiety to include:

- emotion recognition training
- greater use of written and visual information and structured worksheets
- a more cognitively concrete and structured approach
- simplified cognitive activities, for example, multiple-choice worksheets
- involving a parent or carer to support the implementation of the intervention, for example, involving them in therapy sessions
- maintaining attention by offering regular breaks
- incorporating the child or young person's special interests into therapy if possible.

Speech and language problems

10.1.7.10 Do not use neurofeedback to manage speech and language problems in children and young people with autism.

10.1.7.11 Do not use auditory integration training to manage speech and language problems in children and young people with autism.

NICE clinical guidance on behaviour that challenges in children and young people with autism

Anticipating and preventing behaviour that challenges

6.7.1.1 Assess factors that may increase the risk of behaviour that challenges in routine assessment and care planning in children and young people with autism, including:

- impairments in communication that may result in difficulty understanding situations or in expressing needs and wishes
- coexisting physical disorders, such as pain or gastrointestinal disorders
- coexisting mental health problems such as anxiety or depression and other neurodevelopmental conditions such as ADHD
- the physical environment, such as lighting and noise levels
- the social environment, including home, school and leisure activities
- changes to routines or personal circumstances
- developmental change, including puberty
- exploitation or abuse by others
- inadvertent reinforcement of behaviour that challenges
- the absence of predictability and structure.

6.7.1.2 Develop a care plan with the child or young person and their families or carers that outlines the steps needed to address the factors that may provoke behaviour that challenges, including:

- treatment, for example, for coexisting physical, mental health and behavioural problems
- support, for example, for families or carers
- necessary adjustments, for example, by increasing structure and minimising unpredictability.

6.7.1.3 If a child or young person's behaviour becomes challenging, reassess factors identified in the care plan and assess for any new factors that could provoke the behaviour.

6.7.1.4 Offer the following to address factors that may trigger or maintain behaviour that challenges:

- treatment for physical disorders, or coexisting mental health and behavioural problems
- interventions aimed at changing the environment, such as:
  - providing advice to families and carers
  - making adjustments or adaptations to the physical surroundings (see recommendation 4.6.1.9).

6.7.1.5 If behaviour remains challenging despite attempts to address the underlying possible causes, consult senior colleagues and undertake a multidisciplinary review.

6.7.1.6 At the multidisciplinary review, take into account the following when choosing an intervention for behaviour that challenges:

- the nature, severity and impact of the behaviour
- the child or young person's physical and communication needs and capabilities
- the environment
- the support and training that families, carers or staff may need to implement the intervention effectively
- the preferences of the child or young person and the family or carers
- the child or young person's experience of, and response to, previous interventions.

Psychosocial interventions for behaviour that challenges

6.7.1.7 If no coexisting mental health or behavioural problem, physical disorder or environmental problem has been identified as triggering or maintaining the behaviour that challenges, offer the child or young person a psychosocial intervention (informed by a functional assessment of behaviour) as a first-line treatment.

6.7.1.8 The functional assessment should identify:

- factors that appear to trigger the behaviour
- patterns of behaviour
- the needs that the child or young person is attempting to meet by performing the behaviour
- the consequences of the behaviour (that is, the reinforcement received as a result of the behaviour).

6.7.1.9 Psychosocial interventions for behaviour that challenges should include:

- clearly identified target behaviour
- a focus on outcomes that are linked to quality of life
- assessment and modification of environmental factors that may contribute to initiating or maintaining the behaviour
- a clearly defined intervention strategy that takes into account the developmental level and coexisting problems of the child or young person
- a specified timescale to meet intervention goals (to promote modification of intervention strategies that do not lead to change within a specified time)
- a systematic measure of the target behaviour taken before and after the intervention to ascertain whether the agreed outcomes are being met
- consistent application in all areas of the child or young person's environment (for example, at home and at school)
- agreement among parents, carers and professionals in all settings about how to implement the intervention.

Pharmacological interventions for behaviour that challenges

6.7.1.10 Consider antipsychotic medication for managing behaviour that challenges in children and young people with autism when psychosocial or other interventions are insufficient or could not be delivered because of the severity of the behaviour. Antipsychotic medication should be initially prescribed and monitored by a paediatrician or psychiatrist who should:

- identify the target behaviour
- decide on an appropriate measure to monitor effectiveness, including frequency and severity of the behaviour and a measure of global impact
- review the effectiveness and any side effects of the medication after three to four weeks
- stop treatment if there is no indication of a clinically important response at six weeks.

6.7.1.11 If antipsychotic medication is prescribed:

- start with a low dose
- use the minimum effective dose needed
- regularly review the benefits of the antipsychotic medication and any adverse events.

6.7.1.12 When choosing antipsychotic medication, take into account side effects, acquisition costs, the child or young person's preference (or that of their parent or carer where appropriate) and response to previous treatment with an antipsychotic.

6.7.1.13 When prescribing is transferred to primary or community care, the specialist should give clear guidance to the practitioner who will be responsible for continued prescribing about:

- the selection of target behaviours
- monitoring of beneficial and side effects
- the potential for minimally effective dosing
- the proposed duration of treatment
- plans for stopping treatment.

Adults

The following extracts on adults are from the National Collaborating Centre for Mental Health (2012) *The NICE Guideline on Recognition, Referral, Diagnosis and Management of Adults on the Autism Spectrum*. Leicester and London: The British Psychological Society and The Royal College of Psychiatrists.

The extracts are reproduced with permission from the British Psychological Society and the Royal College of Psychiatrists.

NICE guidance on interventions for adults on the autism spectrum

Psychosocial interventions for the core symptoms of autism

9.3.1.1 For adults with autism without a learning disability or with a mild to moderate learning disability, who have identified problems with social interaction, consider:

- a group-based social learning programme focused on improving social interaction
- an individually delivered social learning programme for people who find group-based activities difficult.

9.3.1.2 Social learning programmes to improve social interaction should typically include:

- modelling
- peer feedback (for group-based programmes) or individual feedback (for individually delivered programmes)
- discussion and decision-making
- explicit rules
- suggested strategies for dealing with socially difficult situations.

9.3.1.3 Do not provide 'facilitated communication' for adults with autism.

9.3.1.4 For adults with autism of all ranges of intellectual ability who need help with activities of daily living, consider a structured and predictable training programme based on behavioural principles.

9.3.1.5 For adults with autism without a learning disability or with a mild to moderate learning disability, who are socially isolated or have restricted social contact, consider:

- a group-based structured leisure activity programme
- an individually delivered structured leisure activity programme for people who find group-based activities difficult.

9.3.1.6 A structured leisure activity programme should typically include:

- a focus on the interests and abilities of the participant(s)
- regular meetings for a valued leisure activity
- for group-based programmes, a facilitator with a broad understanding of autism to help integrate the participants
- the provision of structure and support.

9.3.1.7 For adults with autism without a learning disability or with a mild to moderate learning disability, who have problems with anger and aggression, offer an anger management intervention, adjusted to the needs of adults with autism.

9.3.1.8 Anger management interventions should typically include:

- functional analysis of anger and anger-provoking situations
- coping-skills training and behaviour rehearsal
- relaxation training
- development of problem-solving skills.

9.3.1.9 For adults with autism without a learning disability or with a mild learning disability, who are at risk of victimisation, consider anti-victimisation interventions based on teaching decision-making and problem-solving skills.

9.3.1.10 Anti-victimisation interventions should typically include:

- identifying and, where possible, modifying and developing decision making skills in situations associated with abuse

- developing personal safety skills.

9.3.1.11 For adults with autism without a learning disability or with a mild learning disability, who are having difficulty obtaining or maintaining employment, consider an individual supported employment programme.

9.3.1.12 An individual supported employment programme should typically include:

- help with writing CVs and job applications and preparing for interviews
- training for the identified work role and work-related behaviours
- carefully matching the person with autism with the job
- advice to employers about making reasonable adjustments to the workplace
- continuing support for the person after they start work
- support for the employer before and after the person starts work, including autism awareness training.

Biomedical (pharmacological, physical and dietary) interventions and the core symptoms of autism

9.3.1.13 Do not use anticonvulsants for the management of core symptoms of autism in adults.

9.3.1.14 Do not use chelation for the management of core symptoms of autism in adults.

Summary of recommendations

9.3.1.15 Do not use the following interventions for the management of core symptoms of autism in adults:

- exclusion diets (such as gluten- or casein-free and ketogenic diets)
- vitamins, minerals and dietary supplements (such as vitamin B-6 or iron supplementation).

9.3.1.16 Do not use drugs specifically designed to improve cognitive functioning (for example, cholinesterase inhibitors) for the management of core symptoms of autism or routinely for associated cognitive or behavioural problems in adults.

9.3.1.17 Do not use oxytocin for the management of core symptoms of autism in adults.

9.3.1.18 Do not use secretin for the management of core symptoms of autism in adults.

9.3.1.19 Do not use testosterone regulation for the management of core symptoms of autism in adults.

9.3.1.20 Do not use hyperbaric oxygen therapy for the management of core symptoms of autism in adults.

9.3.1.21 Do not use antipsychotic medication for the management of core symptoms of autism in adults.

9.3.1.22 Do not use antidepressant medication for the routine management of core symptoms of autism in adults.

Please note: NICE periodically updates its clinical guidance on issues such as autism. Please check the NICE website at www. nice.org.uk for details of the most current guidance.

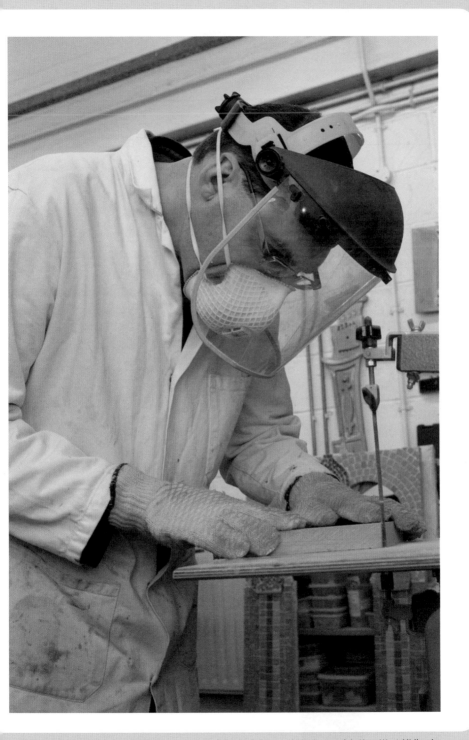

Section 4

Appendices

Introduction

These appendices provide a range of information, including personal accounts of living with autism, as well as lists of useful organisations, websites and publications.

Appendix 1: Personal perspectives

A person on the autism spectrum

We asked the Goth what he would say to other people on the autism spectrum.

Please note: The views he expresses are his own and the interventions he mentions should not be treated as recommendations.

'"They" say the problem is social communication and social interaction. What I'm aware of is the vast number of details that have to be sorted through, consciously or instinctively, in order to communicate and interact. That takes time and rushing it is stressful (trying to fit 20 minutes' work into 10 is stressful for anyone, and this goes on all the time you're interacting with people). No one is prepared to give you time, so you try jumping in with your best guess, or something that just feels like a good idea, and then you're rude to someone.

Being rude to people, or even just odd, is very stressful. People assume you're doing it deliberately, that you are a nasty person who enjoys ruffling people, and they treat you accordingly. It is impossible to explain or excuse yourself as no one believes your version of events. Even 'they' don't.

All the stresses add up to breaking point. Anything I can do to reduce my stress makes a big difference. So cut down on any foods you're intolerant of. At least 10% of people (that's all people, not just autists) have food intolerances, but many people just put up with it and call it indigestion, bloating, or irritable bowel syndrome (IBS). Cut down on the foods that are causing the problem and the unpleasant symptoms go away, along with a bit of stress, and that's enough to make a big difference, particularly with sleep. Onions, grapes, apples, citrus fruits and cheese are common intolerances (they all contain substances that form a group called the FODMAPs), along with the more well-known ones: gluten, dairy and salicylates.

Sensory sensitivities, whether over-sensitive or under-sensitive, are stressful in some situations, and I've never met a professional who understands. They talk about a minority being affected, but I've never met a member of the unaffected "majority" – I've met many people who didn't realise their sensations were different to the norm, though – and they talk of being either over- or under-sensitive, but people are often both at the same time, such as being over-sensitive to light touch and under-sensitive to a firm grasp. Cut down on the situations made stressful by your senses, like public transport at busy times, or wearing the clothes you're expected to wear. People already think you're odd – looking eccentric often makes life easier!

Another way to cut down on stress is to simplify your life. Get rid of things you don't use (I make exceptions for books and music); when I'm home I eat the same meals each week; I have a small wardrobe which I cycle through in turn. Concentrate on doing things to make you happy, not having things. Cultivate your own enjoyment of walking in green spaces: walking (except along polluted roads) is surprisingly good exercise for both body and mind. All of this frees up your energy for tackling your real problems: loneliness, employment (paid or not) and bureaucracy.'

A parent of a child on the autism spectrum

We asked Jenny Maher, a mother of a child on the autism spectrum, what she would say to other parents of children on the autism spectrum.

Please note: The views she expresses are her own and the interventions she mentions should not be treated as recommendations.

'My son Ciaran was diagnosed with autism aged three after being referred for a multidisciplinary assessment by our health visitor. This involved being seen by several professionals in a group setting, including a teacher, nursery nurse, speech therapist and occupational therapist. They wrote a report which was then used by a paediatrician to make a diagnosis.

My husband and I knew there was something wrong as Ciaran's development and speech was delayed. He was also very self-directed and was always on the move. However, we still found it difficult to come to terms with the diagnosis and considered getting a second opinion. The paediatrician didn't offer us any help or support, she just said: "You'll get help when he goes to school". It would have been great if she had been more sympathetic to us as parents and taken the time to explain a little bit about autism to us or given us a pack of useful contacts.

It's difficult to take in what a professional has to say once you hear the word "autism" and we spent a few days feeling quite bewildered and unsure of what the future would now look like.

We decided to do our own research and look at organisations that could help. We bought books on autism and read websites. I went on a Cygnet course through Barnardo's, which was very useful. It helped me to understand more about my son's sensory needs and it was great to meet other parents in the same situation and get the chance to ask their opinions on how to handle certain situations.

It was and still is very important to us as a family to find and use interventions that can help us make sense of our son's behaviour and connect with him. As well as Cygnet, I've been on other autism awareness courses that have helped me to change some of the ways that I phrase things, for example, saying "not now" instead of "no". It's also made me aware that special interests can be used as a motivating tool, so we might let him watch a favourite film or go to a favourite place as a reward for good behaviour. I also sometimes pretend to tell him things via his favourite cowboy toy, either doing the voice or saying his toy wants to go somewhere, to encourage good behaviour or to engage with a particular activity.

We tried setting a rule on one of his negative behaviours by telling Ciaran that he was allowed to swear but could only do it in his bedroom. We were really pleased as this worked pretty much immediately because he didn't want to make the effort to go upstairs. Some visual resources have been useful, such as a traffic light system for behaviour that we have adopted so that we are using the same strategy at school. I also give him plenty of notice when we are going to go out and tell him where we're going, when, and expected behaviours. As he tends to run off he often wears a wrist strap and we can get him to wear it by asking who he wants to be in charge of putting it on: me or his dad, which makes him feel in control.

Perhaps the hardest thing about Ciaran's condition as he got older was watching some of our friends drop away. The best thing was knowing that we had a small group of amazing friends and family who accepted us just as we were and could sympathise with us when Ciaran went on the rampage and trashed the house or just couldn't stay still while we were trying to enjoy a day out.

My advice for parents of children who are newly diagnosed is to take your time to take the news in and try to get as much information as possible. Find organisations that will support you and give you advice, lean on any friends and family who will let you and go on any autism awareness courses that are available.

You will probably meet a lot of professionals along the way. Don't be phased by them, take your time to explain things and remember that you are the one who knows your child best. You may feel that you have to fight for support or services. It's not right or fair, but unfortunately it's just part of life. You are your child's best advocate so make sure your voice is heard. Don't let yourself get fobbed off. If you feel like you're getting nowhere take advantage of organisations that offer advice and support. There is a lot of information out there and you won't be the first person who's experienced a particular situation.

Some people describe having a child with autism as an on-going grief process, however, I don't feel that way. He's just turned seven and I've accepted that my son may never be independent, but as long as he's happy then so am I. I try to keep an open mind about him and what he may go on to achieve. The more effort I put into understanding how his autism affects him, the more I can connect with him. His special interests are a great way to engage with him and motivate him. We're also getting used to the kinds of situations that might trigger a melt-down or make him feel stressed.

It's also important to look after yourself. If you're exhausted and upset your child will pick up on it. You're allowed to have some "me time" and to do the things that help you unwind. Look into respite care if that's what you need but make sure you are able to rest and get time to yourself. It will help you to stay positive and it really makes a difference.'

A partner

We asked Rebecca Brown, the partner of Nik who is on the autism spectrum, what she would say to other people.

Please note: The views she expresses are her own and any interventions she mentions should not be treated as recommendations.

My partner Nik was diagnosed with Asperger syndrome around three years ago. Throughout childhood, he was not provided with the help and support he needed and as a result now has few qualifications and little faith in either himself or the education system. Despite this – despite the lack of official qualifications – Nik is an intelligent, well-read man with a range of interesting opinions. He has a good sense of humour and a talent for wordplay.

As a partner, Nik is thoughtful, loyal and loving. Our relationship is strongly based on mutual trust and respect. Although Nik often needs my help and support, especially in social situations, there is nothing one-sided about our relationship; I am more than just a carer and he is more than just a syndrome. Sometimes, it would be fair to say that Nik takes care of me more than I take care of him. Our strengths and weaknesses complement each other really well.

Even if Nik could be 'fixed', I wouldn't want to change him. He isn't broken and I love him just the way he is. Why shouldn't I? Asperger syndrome is just one small part of who he is.

The biggest problems we encounter are the attitudes other people – and sometimes Nik himself – have towards him. I've seen people shy away from Nik or behave patronisingly towards him when we tell them that he has Asperger syndrome. People don't always know what that means in terms of his intelligence or his needs. I've been asked if his condition is infectious or terminal more than once. Equally, I've heard people say that Nik doesn't have a disability since physically he looks very healthy. How do you make someone understand a condition which they cannot see?

Nik himself suffers from depression and low self-esteem. He often struggles to sleep at night and will often have panic attacks. Despite this, he faces day-to-day challenges – and the bigger ones, things which would scare me! – with a combination of determination, bravery and dignity which I personally find inspirational.

Our relationship isn't perfect and we have problems sometimes, our arguments and so on. No relationship is ever going to be perfect. Ultimately, I love Nik very much and his Asperger's doesn't change that.

Appendix 2: Quotes on interventions

This appendix lists some quotes people have made about interventions for people on the autism spectrum.

'People are always looking for the single magic bullet that will totally change everything. There is no single magic bullet.' (Temple Grandin, woman on the autism spectrum)

'The treatment often has more to do with the belief system of the therapist than the needs of the child.' (Lorna Wing, researcher)

'To intervene is to stop something from happening: to prevent or alter a course of events. In the world of autism I believe we must intervene very carefully because to intervene can easily become an act of sabotaging who a person really is.' (Aaron Yorke, man on the autism spectrum and father of a child on the autism spectrum)

'Don't think that there's a different, better child "hiding" behind the autism. This is your child. Love the child in front of you. Encourage his strengths, celebrate his quirks, and improve his weaknesses, the way you would with any child. You may have to work harder on some of this, but that's the goal.' (Claire Scovell LaZebnik, mother of a child on the autism spectrum)

'We need to tailor the techniques to suit the child, not fit the child to the techniques.' (Pat Howlin, researcher)

'One simple test for anybody thinking about using a particular intervention on autistic people is whether you would be happy if autistic people, or anyone else, used the same intervention on you.' (Damian Milton, man on the autism spectrum and father of a child on the autism spectrum).

'We need to see the world from the autistic perspective and apply approaches based on a mutuality of understanding that are rational and ethical – which respect the right of the individual to be different – yet recognises and deals with distress and offers practical help. We should encourage and motivate the person to develop strengths rather than focus on "deficits". This will mean offering opportunity for development while supporting emotional stability.' (Richard Mills, researcher).

'To measure the success of our societies, we should examine how well those with different abilities, including persons with autism, are integrated as full and valued members.' (Ban Ki-moon, Secretary General of the United Nations).

Appendix 3: Evidence levels

This section explains what we mean by the different levels of research found in other chapters of this book.

Please note: The levels of evidence set out in this appendix do not constitute any kind of recommendation about a particular intervention and whether or not it is appropriate for a specific individual on the autism spectrum.

For each level of evidence, the results can either be positive or negative. Positive results mean the evidence suggests the intervention may have a positive impact. Negative results mean the evidence suggests that the intervention does not work.

1. Limited amount of research evidence of sufficiently high quality

This means that we have identified a number of methodologically rigorous studies.

In practice this means at least two good quality randomised controlled trials or one good quality randomised controlled trial and at least three good quality non-randomised controlled trials.

2. Very limited amount of research evidence of sufficiently high quality

This means that we have identified a number of reasonably rigorous studies.

In practice this means good quality controlled trials or randomised controlled trials which are not as rigorous as those above.

3. Extremely limited amount of research evidence of sufficiently high quality

This means that we have identified a number of studies of limited rigour.

In practice this means other types of studies, such as multiple-baseline studies with sufficient participants. It also means controlled trials or randomised controlled trials which are not as rigorous as those above.

4. Weak evidence

This means that we have identified numerous studies but they are all of very low quality.

5. Insufficient research evidence

This means that we have been unable to identify enough studies of a sufficient quality to be able to evaluate this intervention.

In practice this can mean several things:

- we have identified almost no studies at all, that is to say, one or two low quality studies
- we identified numerous studies but they are all of very low quality
- we have identified a number of studies of variable rigour which contradict each other, that is to say, some report positive results and some report negative results with no overall majority on either side.

6. None

This means we have been unable to identify any studies at all published in peer-reviewed journals.

7. Potentially harmful

This means we have identified at least one research study, or a report from a reputable organisation, such as the National Institute for Health and Care Excellence or the US Food and Drug Administration, of one or more significant harmful effects associated with this intervention.

Please note:

- research means peer-reviewed studies published in English-language journals before 1 January 2015
- all research into autism interventions (9,044) is limited at present, at least compared to schizophrenia interventions (57,562); the numbers in brackets are search results from the PubMed database on 1 November 2014
- even if the research suggests that an intervention is effective, it may not work for every person on the autism spectrum.

Further information

In this book: Please see How to use this book (page 11), Chapter 3 (page 38) for information about interventions, Chapter 4 (page 43) for information about how scientists evaluate those interventions, and Section 3 (page 284) for advice on making the decision about whether or not to use a specific intervention.

Website: Please see www.researchautism.net/our-ratings-system for information about the Research Autism rating system, on which ours is based.

Appendix 4: Glossary

Term	Explanation	Page
Asperger syndrome	Term used to describe a form of autism characterised by a lack of language delay and (usually) higher intelligence	p. 22
Atypical autism	Another term for pervasive developmental disorders (not otherwise specified)	p. 23
Autism	Condition characterised by two core features: persistent difficulties with social communication and social interaction, and restricted, repetitive patterns of behaviour, interests, or activities.	p. 17
Autism spectrum disorders	Term used to explain that autism comprises a range of conditions, such as autistic disorder and Asperger syndrome	p. 18
Autistic disorder	Term used to describe a form of autism characterised by early language delay	p. 22
Childhood autism	Another term for autistic disorder	p. 22
Childhood disintegrative disorder	Very rare form of autism characterised by severe regression after the age of two	p. 21
Core features	The two characteristic features currently used to diagnose autism (outlined in the diagnostic manual DSM-5)	p. 17
Controlled trial	Research study which compares a group that receives treatment to a group that receives no treatment or a different treatment (the control group)	p. 47
Dementia infantalis	Another term for childhood disintegrative disorder	p. 21
Diagnosis	The process of determining by examination the nature and circumstances of a condition such as autism	p. 21
DSM	Acronym for the Diagnostic and Statistical Manual of Mental Disorders, a diagnostic manual used in the US and elsewhere	p. 22

Term	Explanation	Page
Disintegrative psychosis	Another term for childhood disintegrative disorder	p. 21
Evidence	Please see Scientific method	
FDA	Acronym for the Food and Drug Administration, a US government agency responsible for protecting and promoting public health through the regulation and supervision of medications and foodstuffs	p. 277
Heller's syndrome	Another term for childhood disintegrative disorder	p. 21
Hypothesis	Theory or idea which would provide a solution to a problem	p. 43
ICD	Acronym for the International Classification of Diseases, a diagnostic manual used in Europe and elsewhere	p. 22
Infantile psychosis	Another term for autistic disorder	p. 22
Intervention	An action (such as a treatment, therapy or the provision of a service) which is intended to help people on the autism spectrum	p. 38
Kanner's syndrome	Another term for autistic disorder	p. 22
Multiple-baseline	Type of study that measures several things before and after an intervention in order to see whether the intervention had any effect on those things	p. 49
Neurodiversity	Idea that diverse neurological conditions, specifically autism, are simply a natural human variation and neurological differences should be recognised and respected as a normal facet of diversity	p. 24
Neurotypical	Term used by some people on the autism spectrum to describe people who are not on that spectrum	p. 24
NICE	Acronym for the National Institute for Health and Care Excellence, a UK agency which provides national guidance and advice to improve health and social care	p. 303

Term	Explanation	Page
Pervasive developmental disorders (not otherwise specified)	Term used to describe individuals who do not fit into the diagnosis of either autism or Asperger syndrome	p. 23
Qualitative	Type of research which is focused on how people feel, what they think and why they make certain choices	p. 49
Quantitative	Type of research which is focused on statistical, mathematical or numerical data	p. 43
Randomised controlled trial	Controlled trial in which the participants are randomly put into either the treatment group or the control group	p. 47
Regression	Process in which children appear to develop normal language and social skills but then lose these with the onset of autism	p. 20
Research	Please see Scientific method	
Scientific method	A body of techniques for investigating phenomena and acquiring new knowledge, as well as for correcting and integrating previous knowledge. It is based on observable, empirical, measurable evidence, and subject to laws of reasoning. All such evidence is collectively called scientific evidence.	p. 43
Statistical significance	If an intervention is statistically significant, this means that the likelihood that the effect was random is less than five per cent, which means it is more likely to be valid	p. 47
Triad of impairments	Three characteristic features used to diagnose autism including social communication, social interaction, and restricted, repetitive patterns of behaviour, interests, or activities. (outlined in the diagnostic manual ICD-10)	p. 22

If you cannot find a term in this glossary, please also see Main index on page 342 and Interventions index on page 344, and the glossary of terms on the Research Autism website at www.researchautism.net/glossary

Appendix 5: Further reading

This section provides details of some key publications on the subject of autism and related issues.

Autism

- Attwood T (Eds) (2014) *Been There. Done That. Try This!: An aspie's guide to life on Earth*. London: Jessica Kingsley Publishers.
- de la Cuesta GC & Mason J (2010) *Asperger's Syndrome for Dummies* (UK edition). Chichester: John Wiley and Sons.
- Fitzpatrick M (2009) *Defeating Autism: A damaging delusion*. London: Routledge
- Jackson L (2002) *Freaks, Geeks and Asperger Syndrome*. London: Jessica Kingsley Publishers.
- King BR (2011) *Strategies for Building Successful Relationships with People on the Autism Spectrum: Let's relate!* London: Jessica Kingsley Publishers.
- Lawson W (2011) *The Passionate Mind: How people with autism learn*. London: Jessica Kingsley Publishers.
- Milton DE & Bracher M (2013) Autistics speak but are they heard? *Medical Sociology online*.
- Milton DE (2014) So what exactly are autism interventions intervening with? *Good Autism Practice* **15** (2) 6–14.
- Murray D, Lesser M & Lawson W (2005) Attention, monotropism and the diagnostic criteria for autism. *Autism* **9** (2) 139–156.
- Walsh N & Hurley EH (2013) *The Good and Bad Science of Autism*. Birmingham: Autism West Midlands.
- Weston L (2011) *Connecting with Your Asperger Partner: Negotiating the maze of intimacy*. London: Jessica Kingsley Publishers.

Interventions

- National Institute for Health and Care Excellence (2012)

Autism: Recognition, referral, diagnosis and management of adults on the autism spectrum. London: NICE.

- Agency for Healthcare Research and Quality (2012) *Interventions for Adolescents and Young Adults with Autism Spectrum Disorders*. Rockville, MD: Agency for Healthcare Research and Quality.
- National Autism Center (2009) *National Standards Project: Addressing the need for evidence based practice guidelines for autism spectrum disorders.* Randolph, MA: National Autism Center.
- National Institute for Health and Care Excellence (2013) *The Management and Support of Children and Young People on the Autism Spectrum*. London: NICE.
- Agency for Healthcare Research and Quality (2012) *Therapies for Children with Autism Spectrum Disorders*. Rockville, MD: Agency for Healthcare Research and Quality.

Research

- Goldacre B (2009) *Bad Science*. London: Harper Perennial.
- Organization for Autism Research (2003) *Life Journey Through Autism: A Parent's Guide to Research*. Arlington, VA: Organization for Autism Research.
- Pellicano E, Dinsmore A & Charman T (2013) *A Future Made Together: Shaping autism research in the UK*. London: Centre for Research in Autism and Education.
- Sense About Science (2005) I don't know what to believe: Making sense of science stories.

You can find details of other publications including research studies, policy reports and factsheets at www.researchautism. net/autism-publications

Please note: the fact that a publication is listed here does not necessarily mean that we agree with its findings.

Appendix 6: Organisations and websites

Autism

The following organisations and websites can provide more information about autism and related issues.

- Association for Science in Autism Treatment (www.asatonline. org) is an organisation that disseminates information about science-based autism interventions.

- Autism Alliance (www.autism-alliance.org.uk) is a network of autism charities across the UK. Autism Connect (www.autism-connect.org.uk) is the UK's first free social network for people with autism and their families.

- Autism Education Trust (www.autismeducationtrust.org.uk) co-ordinates, supports and promotes effective education practices for children and young people on the autism spectrum.

- Autism Europe (www.autismeurope.org) is an international autism organisation that brings together organisations across Europe to advance the rights of people with autism and their families.

- Autism NI (www.autismni.org) is a parent-led partnership which promotes positive collaboration between parents, professionals and individuals with autism.

- Autism Science Foundation (www.autismsciencefoundation.org) is a US organisation which provides funding for autism research.

- Autism West Midlands (www.autismwestmidlands.org.uk) is a regional autism charity in the UK.

- Autistic Rights Group Highlands (www.arghighland.co.uk) is a group run by and for autistic adults.

- Autscape (www.autscape.org) is an online conference specifically by and for people on the autism spectrum.

- Interactive Autism Network (www.iancommunity.org) is a network which aims to facilitate research by building links within the autism community and provides information on research.

- Interagency Autism Coordinating Committee (www.iacc.hhs. gov) is a US Federal advisory committee which co-ordinates all efforts within the Department of Health and Human Services concerning autism spectrum disorders (ASD).
- Irish Society for Autism (www.autism.ie) is the Irish national autism charity.
- National Autism Center, US (www.nationalautismcenter.org) is an organisation which provides information and resources to families, practitioners and communities.
- National Autistic Society, UK (www.autism.org.uk) is the leading UK charity for people with autism and their families.
- Research Autism (www.researchautism.net) is a UK charity exclusively dedicated to research into interventions in autism.
- Scottish Autism (www.scottishautism.org) is the Scottish national autism charity.

Autism community

The following organisations and websites are run by people on the autism spectrum.

- Aspergers and ASD UK Online Forum (www.asd-forum.org.uk/ forum) is a UK forum for people with Asperger syndrome and other forms of ASD.
- The Autistic Self Advocacy Network (www.autisticadvocacy. org) seeks to advance the principles of the disability rights movement with regard to autism.
- Aspie Village (www.aspievillage.org.uk) UK-based social group for adults with Asperger syndrome and similar conditions.
- Community (www.community.autism.org.uk) UK-based forum run by the National Autistic Society where you'll find people talking about autism and sharing their thoughts, questions and experiences.
- Wrong planet (www.wrongplanet.net) is a web community designed for individuals (and parents/professionals of those) with autism, Asperger's syndrome, ADHD, pervasive development disorders (PDDs), and other neurological differences.

Other issues

The following organisations and websites can provide information about a range of other issues.

- Campbell Collaboration (www.campbellcollaboration.org) is an international research network that produces systematic reviews of the effects of social interventions in crime and justice, education, international development, and social welfare.

- Cochrane Collaboration (www.cochrane.org) is an international organisation that provides systematic reviews to promote evidence-informed health-related decision making.

- Food Standards Agency (www.food.gov.uk) is a statutory organisation which is responsible for food safety and food hygiene across the UK, and which provides free factsheets on various aspects of diet and nutrition.

- Medline Plus (www.nlm.nih.gov/medlineplus) is a source of health-related information produced by the US National Library of Medicine.

- National Center for Complementary and Alternative Medicine (http://nccam.nih.gov) is a US agency for scientific research on the diverse medical and health care systems, practices, and products that are not generally considered part of conventional medicine.

- National Institute for Health and Care Excellence (www.nice. org.uk) is a UK agency which provides national guidance and advice to improve health and social care.

- Sense About Science (www.senseaboutscience.org) is a UK-based charitable trust which aims to encourage an evidence-based approach to scientific and technological developments.

- TRIP Database (www.tripdatabase.com) is a clinical search engine that is designed to allow users to quickly find high-quality research evidence to support their practice.

You can find details of other organisations and websites at www.researchautism.net/links

Appendix 7: Main index

Please also see Appendix 8: Index of interventions on page 344.

Appendix 8: Index of interventions

Please also see Appendix 7: Main index on page 342.

About the authors

Bernard Fleming

Bernard Fleming is the Information Manager at Research Autism, the only UK charity exclusively dedicated to research into interventions in autism. He has worked as an information manager for a number of other charities including the Royal National Institute for Blind People, the Mental Health Foundation and the Foundation for People with Learning Disabilities. He also served on the editorial board of NHS Choices for five years. He currently runs the Research Autism information service, the only autism information service accredited to the NHS Information Standard.

Elisabeth Hurley

Dr Elisabeth Hurley PhD, Bsc, is the Research Officer at Autism West Midlands. She has a PhD in Neuroscience, specialising in the development of the body clock. Since joining Autism West Midlands, she has co-authored *The Good and Bad Science of Autism* (2013) with Dr Neil Walsh and edited the book *Ultraviolet Voices: Stories of women on the autism spectrum* (2014). She provides training on a number of topics including women and girls with autism and putting theory into practice. She is also the co-editor of the *Good Autism Practice Journal*.

the Goth

Diagnosed 13 years ago with high-functioning autism, the Goth has been working as a trainer and advocate in the autism field since then. He also produces and edits *Asperger United* magazine, a free, independent publication funded by the National Autistic Society. His background is farming, physics, linguistics and psychology, and he is also a qualified cabinet-maker. He has advised on two television series that featured autists, co-written *Asperger's Syndrome for Dummies* (2010), and also uses his hearing to advise people on how to get the best sound from hi-fi.

None of the authors has any affiliations or financial involvement that conflicts with the material presented in this book.

About Research Autism and Autism West Midlands

Research Autism

Research Autism was established in 2004 following calls by people with autism and their families for high quality research into autism treatments, therapies and approaches. Our aim is to promote greater inclusion and improve the quality of life of people with autism and their families. We also provide impartial information on the effectiveness of interventions in autism via our website, publications, online Q&As and conferences. We are the only autism charity with NHS Information Standard accreditation. Our focus is exclusively on the day-to-day issues that impact on the lives of people with autism.

Autism West Midlands

Autism West Midlands is the leading charity in the West Midlands for people affected by autism. We exist to enable all people with autism, and those who love and care for them, to lead fulfilling and rewarding lives. Our passionate, expert staff and volunteers work across all age groups and abilities, providing direct support to people affected by autism.

About our sponsor, Dimensions

We gratefully acknowledge support from the sponsor of this book, Dimensions. Without their support we would not have been able to produce this book. That support was freely given and has not influenced the content of this book.

Dimensions

At Dimensions, we support people with autism to live more independently at home and in their community. A longstanding not-for-profit provider for people with autism and learning disabilities, Dimensions supports around 3,500 people and their families across England and Wales.

We are a specialist organisation offering support, training, and consultancy to enable people to live the life they choose. For those with additional behaviour support needs, we employ a large team of behaviour support specialists across the country. Dimensions has experience, expertise and a commitment to achieving positive outcomes and better lives for the people we support.

Acknowledgements

We would like to thank the huge number of people who helped us write this book and ensure that it is both scientifically accurate and easy to read.

We would particularly like to thank David Ellis, Richard Mills and Ashok Roy who read various versions of the entire manuscript and provided valuable feedback throughout the whole process.

We would like to thank members of staff from Autism West Midlands and Research Autism – including Helen Finch, Deepa Korea, Mary Lawrence, Anoushka Pattenden, and Jonathan Shephard – who read various parts of the book and made very helpful suggestions on how to improve it.

We would like to thank members of the Research Autism Scientific and Advisory Committee – especially Carole Buckley, Laura Cockburn, Juli Crocombe, Dido Green, Damian Milton, Jamie Nichols, and Liz Pellicano – who provided invaluable scientific advice on specific chapters.

We would like to thank a number of other people who also provided invaluable scientific advice on specific chapters of the book – including Zoe Connor, Helen Coulter, Sue Fletcher-Watson, Emma Jordan, Daniel Mills, Nicci Paine, Hannah Wright, and Justin Williams.

We would like to thank members of the Research Autism Readers' Panel – including Hilary Dyer, Michael Gray, Gen and Paul Hartup, Sarah Hewitt, Carmen King, Rosie Massey, Ralph Jordan Poseiro Navarro, Shell Spectrum and Karen Wilmshurst – who provided extremely helpful comments about the book and helped us to make it much more user-friendly.

We would like to thank staff at the National Autistic Society – especially Mary Draffin and her team – who have provided extremely useful information on autism and related issues over a number of years.

We would like to thank our Patron, Jane Asher, for writing the preface.

We would like to thank Catherine Ansell-Jones and the rest of the team at Pavilion Publishing and Media Ltd.

And finally, we would like to thank the Goth, Jenny Maher and Rebecca Brown for their personal perspectives.

Notes

Notes